616/90

Flamingos

Flamingos

MALCOLM & CAROL OGILVIE

ALAN SUTTON
1986

Alan Sutton Publishing Limited
Brunswick Road · Gloucester

First published 1986

British Library Cataloguing in Publication Data

Ogilvie, M.A.
Flamingos.
1. Flamingos
I. Title   II. Ogilvie, Carol
598'.34   QL696.C56

ISBN 86299-266-4

Typesetting and origination by
Alan Sutton Publishing Limited
Photoset Palatino
Printed in Great Britain

Contents

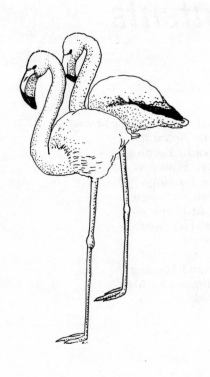

Preface

Flamingos have long been kept in captivity and have always proved very popular with visitors to zoos and bird gardens. Equally, they have a very strong attraction for visitors to those parts of the world where they occur in the wild, whether those visitors are normally keen on birds or not, such is the marvellous spectacle which they so often present.

The last 30 years have seen a steady upsurge in interest in Flamingos both in captivity and in the wild. A number of zoos have become able to breed Flamingos, though even now rather few establishments manage it at all regularly, and that only with three of the six kinds. However, the presence of such accessible breeding colonies has stimulated studies on them by biologists, which have complemented studies being carried out on wild birds in the Caribbean, the Mediterranean, and in East Africa.

The growing awareness of the many threats posed to wetlands of all kinds throughout the world has also played a part in bringing Flamingos more to the forefront of attention. Some of their haunts seem very safe from such damaging prospects as drainage or pollution, with which so many wetlands are threatened. At first sight, there do not seem many actions of man that can harm a highly saline lake several hundred square kilometres in extent. Nevertheless, there have been a number of instances of Flamingo haunts facing drastic change through the establishment of commercial salt extraction works, or the use of meagre water supplies for irrigation. The pressure of growing human populations in some areas is also a serious problem, particularly their effect on the very sensitive breeding colonies.

In 1973, a symposium on Flamingos was held at the headquarters of the Wildfowl Trust, at Slimbridge, Gloucestershire, under the auspices of a number of international conservation bodies, including the International Waterfowl Research Bureau, which is also based at Slimbridge. The Wildfowl Trust has been particularly successful at breeding

Flamingos in captivity, while the I.W.R.B. is actively concerned with the status and conservation of Flamingos worldwide. The symposium was attended by workers from all over the world and the papers read at the meeting, on a wide variety of difference aspects concerning Flamingos, were published in book form. That book (*Flamingos* edited by Janet Kear and Nicole Duplaix-Hall, and published by T. & A.D. Poyser, Ltd.) is now out of print, and in any case was not aimed at a wide non-specialist readership. We hope that this present book is. It draws heavily on published sources, including *Flamingos*, but includes as much up-to-date knowledge as has been available to us. In this connection we would particularly like to thank Dr Alan Johnson, of the Tour du Valat Biological Station in the Camargue, who has studied the Greater Flamingos in the western Mediterranean for many years, and who was extremely generous in sharing the results of his very extensive researches. We are also very grateful to Dr Derek Scott, who imparted of his unrivalled knowledge of South American wetlands and their birds, and permitted a preview of his *Directory of South American Wetlands*, published in 1986 by I.W.R.B.

As will become apparent to anyone reading this book, there is much still to be learnt about Flamingos. We have only a moderately good picture of the numbers and distribution of the more accessible populations, and a very poor idea of what goes on in the remoter parts of their range. For most large, colonially breeding birds, the question of where and when they are breeding is not too difficult to answer. For Flamingos, this always has been, and remains, one of the great conundrums of ornithology. And without this, very basic, information, it is hardly surprising that other equally important knowledge, on trends in numbers, and the effects of various factors on breeding success, and thus the urgency of the need for conservation measures, is equally lacking, and can only be supplied by the carrying out of more studies on the birds in the wild.

In the same way, the need for zoos and bird gardens to limit their taking of Flamingos from the wild to maintain their captive stocks, a need based on both moral and conservation grounds, obliges them to increase their ability to breed Flamingos in captivity. The successes achieved so far have been greatly boosted by careful study of the precise requirements of the birds, and further work in this direction should more than repay the effort involved.

The fact that there is so much still to be discovered about Flamingos almost certainly contributes to their magic and mystery. There seems little or no danger that we will soon, or indeed ever, learn all there is to know about them, and in the meantime we can marvel at and enjoy them, while at the same time making sure that both they and their remote and inhospitable haunts are secure.

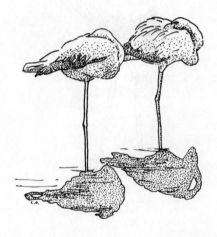

CHAPTER 1

Introduction to the Flamingos

Early history

There can be few more bizarre birds than the Flamingo, yet few more attractive in colouring, or more awe-inspiring in the sheer size and drama of its massed flocks. Standing up to six feet tall, with its long slender neck and matchstick legs, the Flamingo can be likened in design to the Giraffe, improbable and ungainly, yet with a certain elegance of movement. However, its delicate pink and flaming red plumage, set off by jet black wing-tips, ensures that the Flamingo is regarded as an object of beauty rather than just curiosity, whether stalking across the lawns of a small bird garden or spread in hundreds of thousands like pink foam along the shores of a tropical lake.

Man's fascination with the Flamingo's appearance has been greatly increased by the mystery surrounding so many of its breeding habits. Even in such well-known Flamingo haunts as the Camargue in southern France, or the East African lakes, the simple facts of where and when, or indeed whether, the Flamingos were breeding, have only very recently been discovered. In these areas, as well as in other parts of the world where Flamingos occur, including India, South Africa, and South America, the birds have defended their secrets by keeping to remote and inaccessible spots behind barriers of mud, swamp, and desert. Naturalists and photographers probing to get past these obstacles have often spent several years before bringing their quest to a successful conclusion, even risking their lives in the process.

Although a bird of such mystery, the Flamingo has been known to Man for thousands of years, and even worshipped at times. Among the Neolithic cave paintings in southern Spain there is an accurate representation of a Flamingo drawn by a Stone Age artist in around 5000 BC. The Egyptians used the Flamingo as one of their hieroglyphic symbols, to indicate the colour red. They also regarded it as the living embodiment of the sun-god Ra, though in this instance the Flamingo may have been a substitute for the Phoenix, the mythical, and magical, bird which lived in the Arabian desert. There was just a single Phoenix, of great beauty, which lived a span of 500 years. Then it built a funeral pyre, fanned it with its wings, and rose again, reborn from the ashes.

The Phoenix was usually described as being a very brightly coloured, often vivid red, bird, and indeed the Greek word for crimson-red is *phoinix*. Hence the transference to the Flamingo becomes easy to understand. The legend of the Phoenix/ Flamingo survived into the first years of the Christian era, when the cross-like silhouette of the flying Flamingo was taken as a sign by the early Christians, for whom the Phoenix story already had a symbolic significance because of the resurrection of Christ.

Phoenician traders brought dried Flamingo skins to Cornwall and exchanged them for tin, claiming that the skins were those of the Phoenix, and hence objects which would endow their owner with long life. How they overcame the problem of there thus having to be more than one Phoenix, and mortal at that, is not related. These and other stories show how the Phoenix and the Flamingo became inextricably intertwined, so that when scientific Latin names were being chosen to designate the Flamingos, the root of Phoeni- was somehow inevitable. The Flamingos are placed in the Order Phoenicopteriformes and the Family Phoenicopteridae, within which there are three genera: *Phoenicopterus, Phoeniconaias,* and *Phoenicoparrus,* to which we will return later.

The Romans, not untypically, found a gastronomic use for Flamingos, regarding the tongue as a great delicacy. The historian Pliny, in his *Historia Naturalis,* notes: 'Apicius, the most gluttonous of gorgers, has informed me that in his view the Flamingo's tongue is of the most exquisite flavour.' Flamingos' tongues were ranked at Roman banquets on the same level as the brains of peacocks and pheasants, and the flesh of lampreys. There are references to the culinary preparation and eating of Flamingos in Roman literature spanning two centuries. Given the quantities that must have been required to grace the banqueting tables over such a period of years, it is perhaps surprising that the Flamingo survived around the Mediterranean into modern times, though it may well have been far more widespread and numerous in the region than it is today.

After the Romans there was a long gap of many centuries during which published reports concerning Flamingos are few and far between. It was the 16th century before Flamingos were again mentioned in writings at all regularly. Travellers and explorers brought back reports of the birds as well as specimens. They were found in parts of Asia and Africa, and then in the Americas. Indeed there were rather more records of them from America than there were from Europe, leading Oliver Goldsmith to remark: 'This extraordinary bird is now chiefly found in America; but it was once known on all the coasts of Europe.' He went on to comment on how shy and difficult to approach the bird was and how it had been driven from inhabited areas by Man, being then only found in areas with few people. This is one of the earliest observations on a state of affairs which has persisted to this day.

During the 17th, 18th, and 19th centuries, the existence of what are now widely accepted to be six different kinds of Flamingo in the world became known and understood, though rather more varieties were described, only to be lumped in with one of the original forms after a while. The various plumages were for the most part obtained and described during this period, and illustrations appeared in the great early natural history books, such as those by Audubon and Buffon. Much, though, remained unknown or only guessed at, and was to remain so right down to the present day.

Flamingos and their relations

The relationships between different kinds of birds and animals is one of considerable interest, not just to the professional workers in this field, the taxonomists, but also to a wider audience. The question of just which group of birds the Flamingos are most closely related to, the herons and storks, or the ducks, geese, and swans, or some other species, is very commonly asked, but not necessarily easy to answer. There are a number of ways of examining the problem, including looking for common fossil ancestors, and for shared characteristics of internal and external anatomy, of growth and development patterns. It is even possible to use external parasites, which in many cases seem to have evolved along with their hosts so that the feather-lice of closely-related birds are themselves more closely related than to those living on more distant relatives.

There are actually three reasonable possibilities for the evolution of the Flamingos. Firstly, there is quite a lot of evidence put forward, mostly anatomical, that the Flamingos are related to the storks and herons. Thus the structure of the down on the

Greater Flamingos

young chick, and such internal matters as the shape of the pelvis and the ribs, are all reputedly quite similar to those of the stork family. Secondly, there are also a number of features which are claimed to be like those of the wildfowl, and so suggesting a closer link with that group of birds. For example, the young are well covered with a thick coat of down when they hatch, and are also capable of leaving the nest within a few hours. Other aspects of their structure, such as having webbed feet, are more like the wildfowl than the storks, and their feather-lice, too, are closer to those of the wildfowl.

The third possibility, which has only recently been put forward together with some excellent evidence involving the fossil record, the skeleton and muscle structure, and behaviour, is the theory that Flamingos are actually most closely related to a small group of waders, which include the Avocet and Oystercatcher, but have become rather similar in a number of ways to both the storks and the wildfowl by what is known as convergent evolution. They look like these other birds not because of some shared ancestor, but because apparently similar structures of skeleton or feathering are needed to cope with the similar situations in which all three groups of birds live.

This is a subject over which taxonomists will continue to

argue, putting forward theory and counter theory at the drop of
a hat. Certainly there is great scope for argument and debate if
anyone tries to be too dogmatic in stating to which group of
birds the Flamingos are most closely related. Some waterfowl
gardens have no doubt tried to justify their inclusion of Flamingos in their collections by saying that they are just a different
kind of waterfowl, while privately acknowledging that what is
perhaps more important is that Flamingos are popular with
visitors! Other zoos house their Flamingos near the storks and
herons, on the basis of putting look-alikes close to each other. In
the end, of course, it does not really matter at all, but next time
you look at a Flamingo try thinking of it as an over-elongated
Oystercatcher and see whether you think you agree with the
latest theory.

The different kinds of Flamingos

Not all Flamingos are exactly the same. Some are larger than
others, some more brightly plumaged. Six different kinds of
Flamingo have been described and are commonly accepted.
Others have been proposed from time to time, but have not
stood the test of closer examination. But although everyone is
generally agreed on six kinds there is still disagreement on
whether all six should be regarded as separate species or
whether some are merely subspecies. The usual test of a species
is that if two different ones are brought together they will not
interbreed, whereas subspecies or forms of a single species will
do so. This is a difficult test to apply and anyway subject to
numerous exceptions.

On the basis of many similarities of structure and habits it is
now generally felt that the two largest Flamingos, the Caribbean
(sometimes also called the Rosy or Cuban Flamingo) and the
Greater, are subspecies of a single species with the scientific
name of *Phoenicopterus ruber*. *Phoenicopterus* is derived from the
Greek, and means 'crimson-winged', the association with the
Phoenix and the colour red having already been mentioned;
ruber also means red, or bright red. The almost scarlet Caribbean
Flamingo is known as the nominate subspecies with the subspecific name of *ruber*, the same as the specific name, to become
in full *Phoenicopterus ruber ruber*. The Greater Flamingo has the
first two names the same, because it is the same species as the Caribbean Flamingo, but with the addition of a different subspecific
name, in this instance *roseus* – again indicating red or rather pink,
thus reflecting the fact that it is quite a bit paler in colour.

The Chilean Flamingo is sometimes treated as another subspecies with the Caribbean and Greater Flamingos, but recent studies have indicated sufficient differences, particularly in its behaviour, for it to warrant consideration as a full species, still *Phoenicopterus*, because it is clearly closely related to the other two, but with the specific name *chilensis*, meaning 'from Chile', though it occurs in other parts of South America, too.

The Lesser Flamingo has sometimes been put in the same genus, *Phoenicopterus*, as the larger kinds, but it is really rather distinct in a number of ways, including anatomy, and so nowadays is put in its own genus, *Phoeniconaias*, which has the delightful translation of 'crimson water-nymph'. Its specific name *minor* is pretty self-explanatory.

The last two kinds of Flamingo are placed in a third genus, *Phoenicoparrus*, indicating that they are more closely related to each other than to any of the other kinds. The suffix *parrus* derives from the South American Indian word *Parrina* meaning 'birds with long legs'. The two species are Andean, with the appropriate specific name of *andinus*, and James', with the scientific name *jamesi*. Mr Berkeley James was the lucky man who was immortalised in this way, and he achieved it in time-honoured fashion by bringing back the first specimen (a dead bird) to the British Museum, where the taxonomist who recognised it as a new species and published the details chose to call the bird after its finder. There is a code of practice, nowadays mostly adhered to, which prevents taxonomists calling birds or animals after themselves!

Why are flamingos tall and pink?

A comparison between the Giraffe and the Flamingo was made earlier in this chapter. Another comparison is possible because both appear to have excessively long legs raising them well off the ground, and then have to have exceptionally long necks in order that their mouths can reach the ground again! In actual fact, of course, the Giraffe, although it does graze at ground level, principally uses the combination of its long legs and long neck to browse from trees, reaching vegetation out of reach of other herbivores. Similarly, the Flamingo uses its long legs to wade into water much deeper than other wading birds can manage, and further uses its long neck to reach to the bottom mud from which it sifts food. Flamingos do also feed in very shallow water, and here the length of the neck permits a side-to-side sweeping action which greatly increases the volume

Greater Flamingos swimming. The young are about 6 weeks old

of water and mud that can be sifted at each step.

Although the Flamingo's neck is one of the longest in the bird world it is not made up of a great many more vertebrae than in other birds. Indeed look closely at a Flamingo and notice how the neck, instead of following a smooth curve, is made up of a series of short straight sections, with a pronounced kink between each. These are the individual vertebrae, 17 of them in all, only one or two more than are found, for example, in the much shorter-necked goose.

The very long legs are made to seem even longer by the virtual absence of concealing feathering at the top of the upper portion, where it emerges from the body. In many other species the feather-covered muscular part of the 'thigh' extends well down towards the 'knee'. (What appear to be the thigh and knee in birds are actually the equivalents of man's shin and ankle.) This lack of feathering is an additional way of extending the depth to which Flamingos can wade into water and mud. They can often be seen with the water practically lapping their bellies.

Flamingos' feet are quite small for the size of the bird. They are webbed between the three forward-pointing toes, and there is a vestigial hind toe in some species, slightly raised up above the ground, which does not seem to perform any very obvious function. The webbed feet, as well as being useful in supporting the Flamingos when they are walking on soft mud, enable them to swim quite readily. In the wild, whole flocks can often be seen swimming, feeding in water beyond wading depth. They float buoyantly, high on the water, often in dense packs. Swimming is rather less commonly seen in captivity, usually because the ponds are not deep enough, and anyway contain little or no suitable natural food.

Despite the long legs and long neck, there is nothing ungainly about Flamingo movements. They have a considerable grace when walking, probably helped by the way the head and neck are held quite still in relation to the rest of the body. Flamingos can also run well, doing so both in group displays, and when threatened by danger. Unless there is a wind blowing, flight is usually preceded by some running steps, then as the wings begin flapping the bird lifts quite easily into the air. Landing is a reverse of the procedure, the bird touching down and then running several paces. Taking off from and landing on water seems to be very uncommon, being almost certainly rather difficult to accomplish.

Flamingos fly with their head and neck stretched out in front, and their legs trailing behind. This is similar to the attitude adopted by the storks and cranes, for example, whereas herons and egrets fly with their neck tucked back into their shoulders.

Wing-beats are quite rapid, and more or less continuous, though short glides are sometimes interspersed, and may be prolonged when the birds are coming into land. Flocks of Flamingos fly in a variety of formations, often in a loose 'V', rather like geese and swans, but also in long straggly lines and diagonals. Although there is some evidence that there is an aerodynamic advantage for birds flying in regular formation, one very good reason for flying just behind but slightly to one side of the next bird is that it can be seen very clearly, so that changes in direction or height can be instantly followed. At the same time the trailing bird is out of the turbulence caused by the leading bird as it moves through the air. Add several more birds to a pair of Flamingos flying in this fashion and a 'V' or diagonal line is the natural result.

Resting Flamingos may sit down, their legs tucked beneath them, or stand, usually on one leg. It is perhaps one of the commonest questions asked about these birds: why do they stand on one leg? The answer is quite simple: it is more comfortable! And having said that, it is worth pointing out that when we are standing in a relaxed position we nearly always put much more weight on one leg than on the other, and for exactly the same reason. It is presumably the apparent incongruity of these tall birds, perched not on two perilously thin-seeming legs, but on just one, which prompts the question, and it is the remarkable frequency of it being asked which leads the oft-importuned zoo-keeper or guide to reply that the main reason is that if the bird were to lift the other leg up it would fall over!

Having one leg tucked up into the feathers is an obvious way of keeping it and the foot warm in cold weather, and preventing excessive heat loss. However, the birds stand on one leg in hot weather, too, so this cannot be the sole reason. Resting birds almost invariably face the wind, thus stopping both the wind and any rain from penetrating their feathers. Flamingos standing on one leg can be seen swaying back and forth as gusts of wind hit them. When resting, the head may be held in front of the body, curled into a tight 'S', or laid along the back, when the bill may be tucked under the loose feathers of the wings. When looking at a group of sleeping birds, notice how some of them have curled their necks to the left, and others to the right. This is obviously an individual preference, just like the way we fold our arms, but whether the direction is constant in the same bird every time is not known.

The striking pink and red plumage of the Flamingos has, not unnaturally, always attracted considerable attention, though it

is only comparatively recently that it has been discovered just
how Flamingo feathers acquire that colouring. The impetus for
the necessary research came from the zoos and bird collections
which had the birds in captivity, but had great difficulty in
keeping them in good colour. Pale, faded Flamingos were
nothing like as attractive to keep, nor for the visiting public to
look at, as those in their full colour, which could be seen in
photographs and films. It was also suspected, quite rightly as it
turned out, that only Flamingos in good colour would breed.
Consequently, investigations started in a number of countries to
try to find out why Flamingos were pink in the wild and how to
maintain them that way in captivity.

The answer to the problem lies in a group of substances called
carotenoid pigments, which occur naturally in a wide variety of
plant and animal life. They are responsible for the red and
orange colouring in many birds, including Flamingos. They
cannot be synthesised directly by the birds, though their structure, and hence colouring effect on the feathers, bill, and legs,
can be changed in the body. Carotenoids are complicated
molecules made up solely of carbon, hydrogen, and oxygen
atoms, though sometimes the last one is absent. They are
synthesised out of these basic building blocks by plants,
including algae, bacteria, and some fungi. Anything eating any
of these also eats the carotenoids. The food chain of the
Flamingos is not a very long one, with the principal foods taken
being the actual algae, as well as many small animals which feed
on the algae, such as shrimps, molluscs and insect larvae. The
microscopic unicellular algae, in particular, represent the
world's greatest source of primary organic material, with their
tremendous capacity for turning the universally present carbon,
hydrogen, and oxygen into a form which can be used by animals
as food.

Different kinds of birds have different ways of dealing with
their intake of carotenoids. In some it is used in its existing form,
or even mainly excreted. In others, including the Flamingos, it is
first converted into a series of pigments which are then depos-
ited in different parts of the body. For example, the commonest
Flamingo pigment is called canthaxanthin, which has been
found in the feathers, the skin of the legs and face, and in the
yolk of the eggs. It appears to be stored in the liver and is carried
round the bird's body in the blood. The actual mechanism of
converting the original carotenoid into a usable pigment appears
to be undertaken by enzymes in the liver, though there is some
evidence from other birds for conversion taking place in the skin
papillae, the cells from which the feathers actually grow.

Trials to find pigment-rich foods for captive Flamingos were carried on alongside the work which eventually showed just which compounds were most important. At various times, zoos have fed their Flamingos on carrots, originally minced but later liquidised to help the birds take them in more easily, grass cuttings, and red salmon-flesh. Nowadays, the problem has been more or less completely solved with the ready availability of artificially synthesised canthaxanthin.

One puzzle remains: how do Flamingos maintain the colouring in their feathers? Shed feathers fade quite quickly, indeed it is probably this that saved the Flamingo from being heavily exploited in the last century by the plume trade, which under the dictates of fashion so devastated many of the world's populations of egrets. Yet Flamingos retain most of their colouring for the life of their feathers. These are changed in a rather irregular manner, anything between twice a year to every other year. The frequency and completeness of the moult probably varies with the age of the bird and whether or not it has bred in a particular year. Thus the feathers on a bird seem not to fade, or to do so only very slowly. Yet the feather, once it has finished growing, is a dead structure, with no blood supply to bring more pigment.

The plot thickens with the observation in zoos where Flamingos breed that adults that were rearing chicks faded quite quickly, almost to white in some cases. This has been linked with the feeding of the chick by the adults using a crop secretion known to be very rich in pigment. However, just as there is no way for pigment to get into a feather once it has stopped growing so there is equally no possibility for the pigment to be extracted again. What may be happening, though, is that the adults, as they rear their young, go through an extensive moult and whether because they are feeding their young, or for some other reason, put very little pigment into their new feathers. As some pairs are certainly back into full colouring by the next breeding season, it has to be supposed that they moult yet again sometime during the winter or early spring. The whole subject would repay detailed investigation.

A further aspect of Flamingo moult which has given rise to disagreement in published accounts is whether they shed all their main flight feathers simultaneously, and so become flightless for a period of a few weeks while the new feathers grow. This is what happens in virtually all the wildfowl species, and the fact that it has been observed quite frequently in Flamingos has been used as evidence to show a relationship between the Flamingos and this group. However, it seems that not all Flamingos go flightless when moulting and that it may be just as typical for them to change their flight feathers gradually, so that they always retain at least some flying ability.

Despite appearances to the contrary, Flamingos are undoubtedly tough birds that have adapted to a range of habitats and conditions which other birds and animals find intolerable. The majority of the lakes where they live have extremely high concentrations of salt, twice that of sea-water or even more, and about the only other life forms present are algae, brine-shrimps, and brine-flies, on which the Flamingos feed. Other lakes are equally saturated with soda, and may have high levels of sulphates and fluoride. Certainly the water they contain is completely unfit for human or domestic animal consumption.

Leslie Brown, who discovered more than anyone concerning the breeding sites of the Lesser Flamingo in East Africa, nearly lost his life wading over the soda mudflats of Lake Natron to try to reach a nesting colony. The skin peeled off his legs so

Lesser Flamingos at Lake Hannington. Their only fresh water supply comes from boiling geysers which they drink at temperatures that would scald the human palate

severely that amputation was even considered, and skin grafts were necessary to repair the worst damage. Yet the Flamingos are apparently impervious to the caustic nature of the water. However, even they appreciate fresher water to drink though here again they demonstrate an extraordinary degree of tolerance.

The only available cleaner water at some of the lakes gushes out of hot springs and geysers. Although the commonest drinking places for the Flamingos are probably where the streams enter the lakes, and so the water has cooled, Leslie Brown observed them several times drinking from close to the source where the water came welling up from underground at a temperature approaching boiling point. The water was so hot that the birds were hopping from one foot to the other, yet they were apparently managing to drink it. When Leslie Brown tasted the water, after letting it cool down, he found that it was at least fresher than in the lake, though still very bitter, like a dose of salts!

CHAPTER 2

Species Accounts

Introduction

In this chapter, each of the six Flamingos is dealt with in turn. A first section describes the adult bird, plus some information on immature plumages, though these are not very well known for any of the kinds. The first account, that of the Caribbean Flamingo, is the fullest in this respect, and the general details are thought to be similar for the other five. Identification is covered, too, both in the wild and in captivity, though it has to be admitted that immatures without accompanying adults can be very difficult.

The combination of colours on the bill and legs is uniquely different in the six kinds and can be relied on even when, for reasons of general health or diet, the plumage colours of the birds are not fully achieved. The following key will help to identify the adults, and older immatures:

1. Bill black and yellow 2
   Bill black and pink or black and red 3
2. Black on bill extending from tip to bend or beyond, rest pale yellow, usually with red spot between nostrils, legs yellow.. Andean
   Bill tip not reaching bend, rest orangey-yellow, usually with red band at base, legs orange-red .... James'
3. Legs pink, with contrasting red 'knees' 4
   Legs pink or red, without contrasting red 'knees' 5
4. Black on bill tip not or barely reaching bend, inner part of upper mandible pink extending back to bare skin round eye, lower mandible often partly red .... Caribbean
   Black on bill extending from tip to beyond bend, rest of bill whitish or very pale pink .... Chilean
5. Bill dark red with black tip, legs bright red .... Lesser
   Bill pale pink, outer half black, legs bright pink ...... Greater

CO

Caribbeans in flight

The second section details what is known about the distribution and numbers for each kind of Flamingo. For three of them, the Caribbean, Greater, and Lesser, there is a considerable amount of information available, though still many gaps in knowledge. For the remaining three kinds, all from South America, there is much less known, and the gaps correspondingly greater.

Flamingos sometimes wander far from their normal range and can turn up in quite unexpected places. However, there are also birds which have escaped from captivity to confuse the issue. Thus, sightings of Caribbean and Chilean Flamingos in Britain and other parts of Europe will always involve escapes. Greater Flamingos in Europe away from the Mediterranean may be escapes or genuine wild vagrants.

Caribbean Flamingo (also called Cuban, Rosy, or American)

Description and identification (see Plates 1 and 4)

This is the most brightly coloured of the Flamingos. Indeed, this is the only Flamingo which has a body that is red all over in the adult plumage; the other species are really pinkish-white with pink or reddish tinges and areas. Note, however, that some birds in captivity can appear much paler because of deficiencies in their diet, or following moult. The whole plumage is suffused with bright orange-red, particularly on the head, neck, and upper breast. The rest of the body is a little paler, except for a crimson patch on the flanks and under the tail. The front half of the wings, both above and below, is deep orange-red. This contrasts strongly with the black primaries and secondaries which form the tip and rear half of the wing. Just the innermost few secondaries, nearest the body, are pink. In flight, the red in front and black behind produce a pattern that is common to all the Flamingos.

When the bird is standing, long drooping wing feathers called scapulars, mainly red and pink, hang over the flanks and tail. The legs are pink, with a bright violet-red 'knee' joint. The bill has a black outer half and an orange middle which grades into yellow at the base of the upper mandible and red on the lower one. The yellow on the upper mandible runs back to surround the eye which is pale yellow. The adult male and adult female appear to be identical, though the male is up to 20 per cent larger. He stands about 1.6 metres tall (5 ft) and has a wingspan of about the same measurement, both rather larger than the female. Males weigh between about 3 and 4 kilogrammes (7–9 lbs), the females averaging about 1 kilo (2 lbs) less.

This adult plumage is not attained in full until the bird is about three or four years old. It starts life as a very pale grey, or almost white, downy chick, with disproportionately large brownish-black legs and feet, and a short, straight, brown-grey bill. One of the peculiarities of Flamingos, compared with other birds, is that the downy young moult at about 4 weeks old into a second downy plumage, which in the Caribbean Flamingo is a fairly uniform ash grey. And only a week or two later, the first feathers of the juvenile plumage begin to appear. The second down coat is probably kept and forms the undercoat to the juvenile feathers. By this time the bill is beginning to grow quite fast and to show a distinct downward curve.

The juvenile Caribbean Flamingo is grey-brown all over, though with a pinkish tinge on the underparts and on the wings. The main flight feathers are black, as in the adult, and those wing areas which are orange-red in the adult are very pale pink or white in the juvenile. The tail, too, has some pink on it. The legs, feet, and bill are still mainly brown. From this plumage the young bird goes through a succession of moults, gradually acquiring more and more red, and becoming closer in looks to the adult. The intermediate plumages show a lot of variation and precise ageing of birds based on the amount of grey feathering that they retain has proved impossible. The last areas to turn red are on the upper side of the wings.

The voice of the Caribbean Flamingo is quite goose-like, both

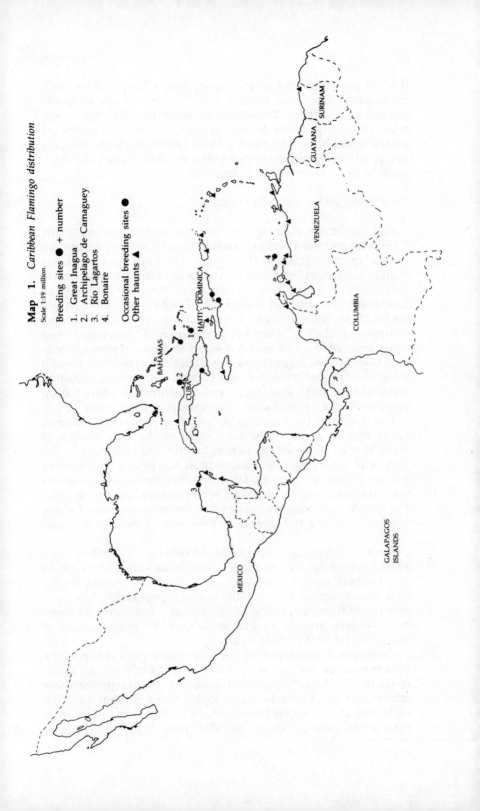

Map 1. *Caribbean Flamingo distribution*
Scale 1:19 million.

Breeding sites ● + number
1. Great Inagua
2. Archipelago de Camaguey
3. Río Lagartos
4. Bonaire

Occasional breeding sites ●
Other haunts ▲

BAHAMAS

CUBA

HAITI

DOMINICA

MEXICO

GALAPAGOS ISLANDS

COLUMBIA

VENEZUELA

GUAYANA

SURINAM

the low gabbling noise which comes from a feeding flock, and, particularly, the nasal, even brassy, 'ka-ha' call given on the ground and in flight. In display, or when showing aggression within a colony, much deeper, grunting or growling notes are added to the honkings. Even a small captive flock can be quite noisy, while a large colony gives off a swelling chorus of sound, audible from a considerable distance.

Distribution and numbers (see Map 1)

The Caribbean Flamingo is confined to the islands of the Caribbean and the mainland coasts around it with an outpost on the Galapagos Islands in the Pacific. The birds on these latter islands have been described as a separate race, mainly because they average a little smaller and paler than the birds in the Caribbean. Throughout their range Caribbean Flamingos are confined to coastal sites, living mainly on saline lagoons, salt-pans, including some being commercially exploited, and other areas of brackish and salt-water shallows. There are only four regular breeding sites of the Caribbean Flamingo, though there were formerly many more. Habitat destruction, including reclamation and drainage, and disturbance have been responsible for their disappearance from several areas.

The largest of the four regular breeding sites is the island of Great Inagua in the Bahamas. Some of the first studies of Flamingos were carried out here at the turn of the century by the American naturalist, F.M. Chapman. It was largely as a result of his work that, some years later, the first protection measures were taken to keep hunters and even just sightseers away from the colony at nesting time. The birds breed on a series of saline lagoons, shifting the precise colony site according to water depth.

Since 1952, regular estimates of the number of breeding pairs at this colony have been made. They have varied from nil, in years of both drought and heavy rain, the latter causing floods, to a maximum of 10,883. The average population has been around 6000 pairs over the whole period. There are also many non-breeders present on Inagua, with some recent counts of about 40,000-50,000 birds in all.

Flamingos forming part of the same population group as the Bahamas birds also occur on Cuba, particularly on the north coast in the Archipielago de Camaguey. Although there are rather few good counts, over 45,000 were present in 1983, including about 10,000 immatures. Breeding takes place in at least some years, with up to 5000 pairs. What are certainly spin-offs from the Inagua colony are small colonies of from 50 to 300 pairs in the Dominican Republic and on Acklins Island in the Bahamas. A few hundred birds winter in Dominica and Haiti. There is a separate population of Caribbean Flamingos on the Yucatan Peninsula of Mexico. The nesting colonies are found in an area called Rio Lagartos in the north-east part of the peninsula. There are about 50,000 hectares (200 square miles) of small estuaries and saline coastal lagoons, no more than 2 metres (6 feet) deep, fringed by mangroves. Over half of it is permanently flooded, the remainder drying out in the dry season. A faunal refuge has been established over the bulk of the area since 1979 specifically to protect the Flamingos.

In 1971, an aerial survey found a total population of just over 12,000 birds, including some 3000 nesting pairs. Since then, breeding has taken place quite regularly with between 300 and 4000 young being reared each year, though in 1982 and 1983 floods destroyed all the nests. However, some 5000 pairs nested successfully in 1984. The total population is put at around 26,000 birds. From Yucatan, the Flamingos disperse along the coasts in both directions for the rest of the year.

The third breeding site is on the island of Bonaire, in the Netherlands Antilles. Flamingos are known to have bred here since at least 1681. Over the last twenty years the number of breeding pairs has varied between 2000 and 2500, while the total population has lain between 7000 and 12,000 birds. However, recent counts from Venezuela where the bulk of the Bonaire birds winter suggest a rather higher total of 17,000.

Venezuela has become more important in recent years as a Flamingo area, largely because a shortage of food on Bonaire forces the Flamingos there to make long feeding flights to the north coast of Venezuela, even at the height of the breeding season. Flamingos may also have bred in at least one locality in recent years. This is also true of neighbouring Colombia, where many hundreds of Flamingos winter.

The Flamingos do not nest every year on Bonaire, probably because of annual differences in water-levels and food availability, but it has been found that provided there are about three successful breeding years in every six or seven, then the population seems to be capable of maintaining its numbers. As well as the main wintering grounds in Venezuela, the Flamingos disperse outside the breeding season along the northern coast of South America, from Colombia to the Guianas, with a few thousand regular in Suriname. The odd straggler has even wandered as far as the mouth of the Amazon.

During the 1960s, the natural salt-lake where the Flamingos

Caribbean scratching

nested was drastically altered by the building of large-scale salt
works. Fortunately it proved possible to provide a sanctuary
nesting area for the birds. A fuller account of this successful
conservation story will be given in the last chapter.

Finally, there is the breeding population of the Caribbean
Flamingo on the Galapagos Islands in the Pacific off Ecuador.
There is not a great deal of information available, partly because
the birds are so scattered, and partly because, unusually for
Flamingos anywhere, they breed in tiny colonies, of no more
than five or ten pairs in each. They occur mainly on Charles,
Indefatigable, Albemarle, and James Islands, with the last-
named the most usual one for nesting. The favoured haunts are
small lagoons just behind the beach. These become flooded at
the highest tides, and then seepage and evaporation leads to a
steadily increasing salinity. There is no fixed breeding season,
nests having been found any time between February and
December.

A reasonably complete census of the Galapagos Flamingos in

1968 found a total of 516 birds, while another in 1976 found 391
adults, 51 juveniles, 21 chicks, and 32 eggs, or a total of 496,
assuming all the eggs hatched. Certainly there was no
suggestion of any trend upwards or downwards in the
population over the period of eight years. Some visitors to the
islands, even in recent years, have reported much smaller
numbers than this, and have stated that the population is
seriously declining or even in danger of extinction. However,
there is no good evidence for large fluctuations and it is more
likely that some birds were missed in remote bays and lagoon.
Though this is a small and completely isolated population, it
appears to be maintaining itself satisfactorily, nonetheless.
There is no evidence of any movement of Flamingos between
the Galapagos and the mainland.

The total of these four population units within the range of
the Caribbean Flamingo amounts to at least 80,000 and possibly
90,000 birds, varying according to whether, or how well, each
unit breeds in a particular year. How this compares with the
past is very difficult to assess, but the American Robert Allen
estimated that in the 17th and 18th centuries, when the Flamingos were first being discovered by Europeans, the population
may have been as high as 95,000. His own estimate for 1956, the
time of his own studies, was 21,500. It is now thought that he
underestimated some of the population groups, while there
have very probably been increases in some of them, too. What is
very clear from all this is that accurate counting of Flamingos is
quite difficult, and made even more so by the occurrence of the
birds in several different countries, some of which, for example,
may not allow aerial surveys or even ground visits by biologists
from other countries.

The quoted figure of Robert Allen for former centuries was
based on knowledge of many more breeding sites than there are
now, though it is quite probable that not all of them were in use
at the same time. The Caribbean Flamingo has certainly ceased
to breed in a number of former sites around the Caribbean and
many of these localities are no longer suitable for breeding.
Fortunately the areas where it still breeds are reasonably secure,
even though there may not be much scope for expansion back
into some of its old haunts.

As a vagrant, the Caribbean Flamingo is seen quite regularly
in the southern states of America, from Texas to Florida, and up
the eastern seaboard. It has also occurred on Bermuda.
However, the presence of a captive flock in Florida, at Hialeah
Park, with many birds there full-winged, leads to the suspicion
that many, if not quite all, of the records will be of escaped or

wandering birds from this flock. A report that Flamingos once
bred on the Florida Keys is now generally discounted.

Greater Flamingo

Description and identification (see Plates 2 and 4)

The Greater and Caribbean Flamingos, being subspecies, are
very similar in size, shape, and structure. The Greater, though,
is much paler with body, head, and neck white tinged with
pink, and the amount of colour varying with age and diet. Even
the pinkest birds, do not ever have the rosy colouring of the
Caribbean. The brightest colouring is on the wing, where the
coverts are crimson, darker above than below, producing, with
the black primaries and secondaries, the typical Flamingo wing
pattern in flight. Pale pink or white plumes trail over the closed
wings, hiding most of the crimson. The legs are pink with
slightly brighter pink joints and feet. The bill has a smaller black
tip than the Caribbean's, not extending as far as the bend, while
the rest of it is pink right back to the bare skin round the yellow
eyes. In other aspects, including voice, measurements, and
weight, the Greater Flamingo is similar to the Caribbean.

The downy young Greater Flamingo is covered in very pale
grey down, being lighter, almost white underneath. It quickly

Greater Flamingos

Caribbean Flamingo

Greater Flamingo

Lesser Flamingo

Caribbean Flamingo

Ad

Juv

Greater Flamingo

Ad

Juv

Ad

Juv

Lesser Flamingo

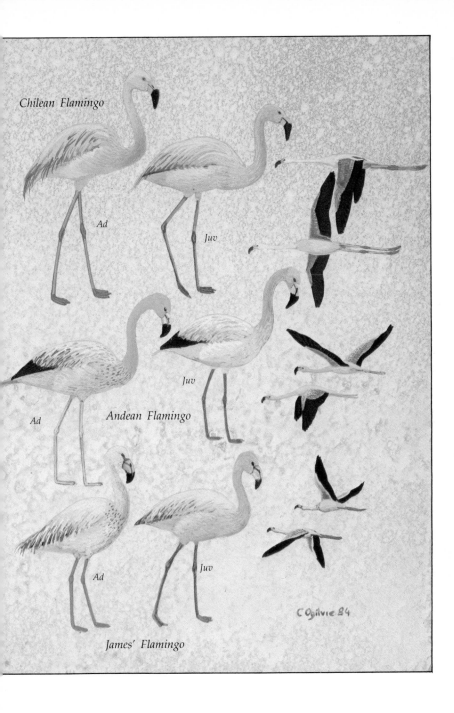

Chilean Flamingo

Ad

Juv

Andean Flamingo

Ad

Juv

Ad

James' Flamingo

Juv

C. Ogilvie 84

Chilean Flamingo

Andean Flamingo

James' Flamingo

moults into a second, darker grey down. The short straight bill and the legs and feet are pinkish on hatching, while the bare skin round the eye is red. However, this soon fades and by the time the chick is about a week old, the bill and face are almost grey, and the legs and feet brownish-black. As the bird grows it develops a grey-brown plumage, rather browner than the young Caribbean Flamingo, faintly tinged with pink on the wings and tail. This is succeeded by an almost white immature plumage on the head, neck, and body, while the wings acquire some of the crimson of the adult. The legs turn pink though the joints and feet remain darker. There is much variation in the development of young Flamingos and determining their age from their plumage is apparently impossible. They are at least two years old, possibly more, before they attain full adult plumage, and probably do not begin to breed until they are four, with the occasional precocious bird starting at three.

Distribution and numbers (see Maps 2 and 3)

The Greater Flamingo has the widest distribution of all the Flamingos. It occurs in the western Mediterranean and down the coast of West Africa as far as Senegal and Guinea Bissau, with a former outpost on the Cape Verde Islands, and from the eastern Mediterranean eastwards through Iran into southern USSR and south-eastwards to India and Ceylon. There are further populations in east and south-west Africa. The main haunts throughout this large range are coastal lagoons and mudflats, but they also occur inland at large, shallow lakes which are either highly alkaline or saline, thus giving them similar conditions as on the coast.

The exact extent of possible separate populations of Greater Flamingos within this large range has not yet been fully worked out. Substantial ringing has been done, particularly in the Camargue in southern France, at Lake Rezaiyeh, Iran, and Lake Turgiz, USSR, with much smaller numbers marked in Spain, Senegal, Southern Africa, and India. Recoveries from these birds, together with information on distribution and numbers at different times of the year, suggest several more or less discrete populations, though with some birds, mainly juveniles, wandering between them. There may also be some sub-groups, based on breeding colonies, within these populations.

The population based round the western Mediterranean is probably the best known, thanks to some intensive studies carried out over many years in the Camargue, plus censuses over much of the rest of the area. The work has included

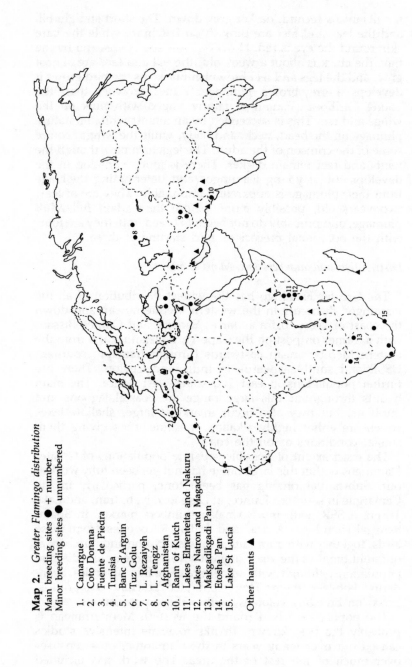

Map 2. *Greater Flamingo distribution*

Main breeding sites ● + number
Minor breeding sites ●
unnumbered

1. Camargue
2. Coto Donana
3. Fuente de Piedra
4. Tunisia
5. Banc d'Arguin
6. Tuz Golu
7. L. Rezaiyeh
8. L. Tengiz
9. Afghanistan
10. Rann of Kutch
11. Lakes Elmenteita and Nakuru
12. Lakes Natron and Magadi
13. Makgadikgadi Pan
14. Etosha Pan
15. Lake St Lucia

Other haunts ▲

providing an artificial nesting island (which will be discussed in more detail in Chapter 6), detailed breeding biology studies, and the regular ringing of young birds just before fledging. The Camargue is the major breeding site for this population, with several thousand pairs breeding successfully each year. However, breeding has not always been so regular nor so successful. The first properly recorded breeding attempt was in 1914, involving several hundred or possibly thousands of pairs. There were certainly earlier attempts than this, including in the 16th and 18th centuries, but there are no firm details. Over the next 31 years, to 1946, there were breeding attempts in 14 years. There are no good records of how many pairs were actually breeding but the number of young reared varied between a few hundred and 2500.

From 1947 and 1963 around 3000 pairs bred each year, rearing on average just over 1800 young. However, from 1954 to 1963 the number of young reared fell to an average of just over 800, even though the number of pairs attempting to breed rose to an average 4000. The best year was 1956 when a record 8000 pairs attempted to breed, but only managed to rear 1600 young between them. Then in 1962 and 1963 no young were reared at all. There followed five years with no breeding attempts whatsoever and it began to look as if the birds might have abandoned the area. However, in 1969 there was successful breeding again, as there has been annually ever since. The number of pairs has been growing steadily, from 3000-4000 in the early 1970s to over 9000 in 1977 and again in 1981. Then in 1983 there were no less than 14,400 pairs, raising an equally record 7200 young.

The knowledge that we have of the Camargue Flamingos in the first half of this century is largely due to the efforts of a Frenchman, Etienne Gallet. Living in the nearby town of Arles, he amassed details of successful breeding years but, wisely, kept much information secret until finally publishing his book *The Flamingos of the Camargue* in 1949. This wonderfully poetic account of the Camargue and the life of the Flamingos was illustrated with fine photographs taken in the colonies. There was historical evidence going back two centuries or more of Flamingos in the Camargue area, including records of birds being killed after getting frozen into ice in severe winters, but no published proof of breeding until Gallet's earliest record of 1914. The year after Gallet's book came out the English bird photographer George Yeates produced his book *Flamingo City* with details of the colony in the years 1947 and 1948 together with excellent pictures in colour and black and white.

The evidence from the long breeding record in the Camargue clearly shows how vulnerable the birds are to serious disturbance of their colony. Foxes and dogs are held responsible for the disruption of breeding in some past years, and if severe enough would often be followed by a non-breeding year, suggesting the birds were loath to return to a site which had been so seriously disturbed. The taking of eggs by people from the surrounding area is known to have partially or completely destroyed several colonies, the last occasion being in 1955.

In recent years the disturbance threat has come more from sightseers, bird-watchers, and photographers, particularly when, in the early 1970s, the nesting colony was only about 500 metres from a public track. Day and night wardening throughout the highly vulnerable incubation period has successfully coped with this problem, while action has also been taken to forbid low-flying aircraft from coming near the breeding birds.

The colony is normally situated on a low island in one of the Camargue lagoons, or etangs. This gives the Flamingos safety from foxes and dogs, unless, as has happened, the water-level drops too far. Alternatively, and more commonly, strong winds, which are very frequent in spring, can cause so much wave action that the nests get flooded out or even washed away. Storms during the winter months can also erode away large areas of the island. The Flamingos themselves compound the problem because their nest-building activities lower the overall level of the island over a period of years. And if the island becomes too small for breeding, or disappears altogether, then the birds are very reluctant to move to a new island immediately. They seem to need a year or two to get used to the idea.

The lagoons in which the Camargue Flamingos nest are part of a system used for extraction of salt, similar to the nesting sites of the Caribbean Flamingo in the Dutch Antilles. The water-levels in the lagoons can be controlled, though this is not always done to the advantage of the Flamingos. However, recently an artificial island was constructed in one of the favoured lagoons to replace one that had largely eroded away and, encouraged by the making of artificial nests to persuade the birds that the island had already been used before, the Flamingos quickly adopted it. More details of this conservation effort will be given in the last chapter. With the increasing numbers in recent years, there are now usually two nesting colonies in the Camague, one on the artificial is land and one on a nearby dyke.

Breeding in Spain by Greater Flamingos seems always to have

been irregular. The first authentic records are from the middle of the 19th century and mainly from sites which have been used down to the present day. Among these have been the famous marismas of the Coto Donana, the marshes at the mouth of the Guadalquivir River in south-west Spain. This is where Abel Chapman recorded a colony in 1883, the first time an ornithologist had seen and described nesting Flamingos anywhere in Europe.

They have bred in the marismas only infrequently since. There were attempts in 1935, 1941, and 1945, but it is not thought that many, if any, young were reared in those seasons. 1935 was a very dry year, and parties of unaccompanied young wandered long distances from the colony, one group being seen 18 kilometres away. In 1941, a very wet year, the nests disappeared quite soon after being built. Then in 1945, Egyptian Vultures were seen preying on the colony and are thought to have caused its failure.

More successful breeding occurred in the marismas in the late 1970s, with several hundred young reared in at least two years, though in 1979 wild boars disrupted the colony, and then floods destroyed most of the remaining nests. Since 1979, several years of low rainfall in south-west Spain have made conditions less good for the Flamingos. Nevertheless, over 2000 pairs managed to breed in 1982, as did some 3700 pairs in 1984.

In 1963, a colony was established at Fuente de Piedra, a shallow, saline lagoon in Andalucia, about 100 kilometres (60 miles) east of the Coto Donana. The birds did not get started until quite late in the season, but were then very successful, with over 2000 young reared to fledging after about 3600 pairs had nested. Interestingly, this first successful breeding in southern Spain for 18 years came in the same year as a breeding failure in the Camargue. It was noted at the time that a lot of adults left the Camargue immediately after their nesting attempt had failed. It seems as though some at least of these moved to Spain and had a second go.

Breeding at Fuente de Piedra has taken place erratically since 1963, with attempts in ten years up to 1984. Sometimes, as in 1964 and 1969, only a handful, less than 50, pairs bred, while in other years the colony was numbered in thousands. Between 1977 and 1979 about 5000 pairs attempted to breed each year, a similar number to the breeding colony in the marismas in those same years. In 1980 and 1981 no birds bred, while in 1982 about 2000 pairs attempted to do so but no young were reared. The reason was a lack of water, both through low rainfall and the use of the inflowing streams for irrigation. Even when there was available water it was suspected of pollution from agricultural run-off and in 1983 this meagre supply was cut-off for a time to be on the safe side. High water-levels between February and April are essential if the birds are to breed successfully, so in 1984 water was pumped into the lagoon from a nearby well and about 5700 pairs of Flamingos responded to this help and bred successfully.

In 1973 a completely new site was occupied, in some salt-pans near Alicante on the Mediterranean coast of Spain. Only about 115 pairs bred, rearing rather few young, but it demonstrated the extraordinary capacity of Flamingos to discover a new and suitable site and to make rapid use of it. Breeding has not occurred at the same place since, but it would appear that conditions are not ideal for regular nesting.

Elsewhere in Iberia, there have been reports of occasional breeding at a number of different localities, including the mouth of the River Tagus in Portugal, at Albufera, near Valencia, Spain, not all that far from Alicante, and on the islands of Ibiza and Mallorca. These are all old records, however, and based on fairly flimsy evidence.

Information on the Greater Flamingo in North and West Africa is, perhaps not surprisingly, even sparser than it is for Spain. Breeding has been recorded in Tunisia, Morocco, and Mauritania, and Senegal in recent years, and formerly on the Cape Verde Islands. In all these countries rainfall is erratic, so that the saline lakes which provide Flamingo breeding sites are both irregular and temporary in their appearance.

The main breeding area in Tunisia is the Chott Djerid, a region of salt-lakes in the south of the country. Here Flamingos bred in 1926, again in 1948 and 1949, and at least occasionally in the 1950s and 1960s. There are few details, but in 1959 it is thought that about 3000 pairs bred, laying their eggs in the middle of February, with between 1500 and 1900 young being seen in July. In 1972, some 10,000 pairs were found breeding on a temporary lake in the centre of the country. There was no sign of them the following year, but over 1000 pairs attempted breeding in 1974 and again in 1976. However, 1974 also saw a massive breeding colony of over 10,000 pairs on the Chott Djerid, though there has been no attempt there since, largely it appears because of the drought conditions which have prevailed in recent years. There has been sporadic breeding elsewhere in Tunisia, but the nests are not infrequently robbed by the local people.

Several thousand Flamingos occur regularly in Algeria, mainly in the east of the country, close to the Tunisian border.

They have never been proved to breed here but it would seem a distinct possibility if the right conditions appeared. Breeding was first proved in Morocco in 1965, though suspected prior to this. The main site is an inland saltlake near Iriki in the south-east of the country. Here there were at least 600 nests in 1965 and about 1500 the following year. Over 500 young were seen in 1968, but there seems not to have been any successful breeding since. On the coast, breeding has been suspected in two different localities, also in the south.

The numbers of Flamingos in the western Mediterranean have been estimated fairly accurately in recent years, and are thought to lie between 60,000 and 70,000. There is some suggestion of an increase over the last decade, not least because of the long run of successful breeding in the Camargue since 1969. However, this is partly based on larger numbers in the French haunts than formerly, and as counts from Spain and North Africa in past years are so sparse, it may just be a redistribution of the population rather than an actual change.

Ringing of young Flamingos has been carried out in the Camargue over many years, particularly in the 1950s, and again in the last few years when individually numbered plastic rings were used in addition to the normal metal bands. The former can be read in the field, and have produced a great deal more information on movements, particularly by different age classes.

There is an exodus from the Camargue from September onwards, with the young of the year moving out almost entirely. They disperse along the French coast and on into southern Spain, and also across the Mediterranean to Tunisia and Algeria, with considerable numbers stopping in Sardinia. Conversely in years when there has been breeding in Spain and Tunisia, flocks of first-year birds have arrived in the Camargue as early as the end of July. This indicates a similar dispersal of young birds from those colonies, which normally have an earlier start to the nesting season than in the Camargue.

Between 2000 and 4000 Flamingos have commonly wintered in the Camargue area, though up until about ten years ago only a few hundred Flamingos remained elsewhere in southern France through the winter. Recently, however, more and more have been staying, with up to 20,000 in some winters, unless driven away by bad weather, such as the exceptional cold of winter 1984–85.

Sightings and recoveries of Camargue-ringed birds have been made in Mauritania and Senegal on the one hand, and in Libya and Turkey in the opposite direction. However, it is difficult to be certain what scale of movement these represent because the chances of sightings from these countries are so much lower than from those bordering the western Mediterranean. The birds may be just stragglers, but there remains the possibility that there is regular movement at least of immature birds.

In the north of Mauritania lies a vast area of shallow seas, mudflats, and scattered islands known as the Banc d'Arguin. Breeding by Flamingos has been proved in four widely spaced years since the first discovery in 1957. The number of pairs involved each time has varied from a few hundred to many thousands, with the maximum in 1982 variously reported between c.10,000 and 16,500. Further south, the Senegal River floodplain holds many Flamingos in the wettest years, but breeding has only been proved twice, in 1976 and 1977, and then only 200 and 115 pairs respectively. In very recent years low rainfall has meant that the river has hardly flooded. Several thousand Flamingos were seen in the Djoudj National Park in Senegal in January 1979, probably displaced from Mauritania.

Flamingos bred a number of times in the last century on the Cape Verde Islands, lying in the Atlantic about 700 kilometres off the west coast of Africa. The last authenticated occasion was in 1898, since when the bird has become merely a vagrant. It seems most likely that a flock of Flamingos must have reached the islands from Mauritania and stayed to breed, but failed to do so often enough or successfully enough to maintain themselves.

There have been a number of attempts to count the Flamingos in the Banc d'Arguin, including from the air. The best estimates date from the early 1970s when over 30,000 were counted in two successive years. Neither survey covered all possible Flamingo haunts in the area and the observers thought that there was a maximum population of 50,000 birds, while more recently it has been suggested that 80,000 might be a better estimate.

The Greater Flamingo occurs in scattered fairly small numbers in the eastern Mediterranean. There are clearly wintering birds in Libya, with recoveries there from ringing in both the Camargue to the north-west and in Iran, far to the east, but information is very sparse. Such information as there is suggests that up to 2000 birds winter there, while so far as is known the birds have never bred.

Flamingos have always been rather rare in Greece, but quite recently there were sightings of a few hundred in the east of the country, probably birds from the Turkish population. Several thousand winter each year on the island of Cyprus, mainly on the salt-lakes at Akrotiri and Limasol. Over the period 1956 to 1978 the average peak at the two sites topped 5500, the bulk of the birds being at Akrotiri. The maximum was as high as 11,000.

The birds arrive in October and November, building to a maximum in early January, departing in late January and during February. Only stragglers remain into April and May, though some years a handful spend the summer. There has been a small number of ringing recoveries on Cyprus of birds marked in Iran, but it is likely that the majority of the wintering flock come from Turkey. A recent proposal to site a sewage treatment works close to the Akrotiri salt-lake has been quashed because of the severe adverse effects it would have had on the Flamingos and other wildlife of the area.

As recently as 1970 a hitherto unknown nesting site of the Greater Flamingo was discovered in northern Sinai, in Egypt. It was spotted from the air, and it was estimated that there were between 500 and 600 pairs, with about 500 young. It is thought that breeding has taken place here since, but there are few details, beyond the knowledge that the Flamingos, like most birds in Egypt, are extremely vulnerable to shooting and other exploitation by the local people.

Another new breeding locality for the Greater Flamingo was discovered recently, this time in Turkey. The main site is at Tuz Golu, a vast inland salt-lake, 1000 metres up on the central plateau. At least 2000 pairs were found breeding here in 1969, and some 5000 in 1970, when there was also a second colony of 1500–2000 pairs on the Sultan Marshes, not far away. Breeding was suspected before the colonies were actually found because it was known that villagers sometimes caught unfledged young ones for food. The species is probably a fairly regular breeder in Turkey, though details are scarce and here as elsewhere the birds are almost certainly not breeding every year.

The high lakes mostly freeze over in winter, forcing the Flamingos to descend to the lowlands. Here the main sites are on the Mediterranean coast in the mouths of the Seyhan and Menderes rivers, as well as on Cyprus. The total Turkish population is estimated to be between 20,000 and 25,000. However, in autumn and winter there have been counts of the order of 40,000–60,000 birds, which must therefore include immigrants from elsewhere. Recoveries of birds ringed in Iran and the southern USSR confirm this, while for good measure there has also been a single recovery in Anatolia of a Flamingo marked in the Camargue.

Moving eastwards, Flamingos have been found wintering in some thousands on Lake Djabboul in northern Syria. These may be Turkish birds, or belong to the Iranian breeding population. Flamingos are found quite widely in Iraq, but recent numbers have generally been quite small, hundreds at most. There are no recent breeding records, though it seems that they have done so in the past. Similarly, there is a breeding report from Kuwait in 1922, but they now only occur there in very small numbers, as they also do along the south side of the Persian Gulf.

The best known Flamingos in this part of the world are those in Iran. A considerable amount of research was carried out into their numbers and movements in the late 1960s and early 1970s, though there is little information for the last few years. Several thousand young birds were caught and ringed, and in addition surveys were made of wintering numbers.

The breeding locality is Lake Rezaiyeh in north-west Iran, not far from the Turkish and Russian borders. This is an enormous,

Greater Flamingo and chicks about one month old

but shallow, salt-lake, over 5000 square kilometres (nearly 2000 square miles) in extent. It contains a great many small islands and banks and it is on these that the Flamingos nest. Breeding was first reported in 1898 but records from then until quite recently are extremely few. Some tens of thousands of birds were present in the mid-1960s, but the first really good estimate of breeding numbers came in 1971 and 1972 when aerial photography was used. Some 15,000 to 20,000 breeding pairs were present both years, together with a further 5000–10,000 non-breeding birds. In the late summer of 1973 a survey revealed 58,500 aduts and 20,000 young, suggesting an even larger breeding population than in the previous two years.

Several thousand Flamingos summer regularly on salt-lakes near Shiraz in southern Iran, not far from the Persian Gulf. There are past records of small breeding colonies here but none were found breeding at any time in the period from 1965 when regular observations were being made. Instead the area is one of the main wintering sites within Iran, with counts of up to 52,500 birds, which are thought to comprise the bulk of the breeding population from Lake Rezaiyeh.

Lake Rezaiyeh itself holds few birds in winter, generally less than 1000. Much larger numbers are found on the south coast of the Caspian, particularly in Gorgan Bay on the east side close to the Russian border, as well as some other smaller wetlands along the coast. Up to 11,000 have been counted in this area, though about 4000 is apparently more usual. Ringing recoveries indicate that the bulk of these birds come from breeding sites in southern Russia. Elsewhere in Iran, small numbers of birds have been found scattered along the south coast as well as in the Persian Gulf. The marshes at the head of the Gulf might once have been suitable for nesting, but are little known and have been fought over extensively in recent years.

Ringing of young Flamingos at Lake Rezaiyeh has produced a wide scattering of recoveries, from Libya, Cyprus, and Turkey to the west, and eastwards to the Indus/Ganges plain of Pakistan and India. There have also been two birds reported from Ethiopia, suggesting movement to the East African lakes. The recovery pattern indicates a wide dispersal of immature Flamingos from Iran in their first winter, and this is reinforced by the winter counts in Iran which found very few young birds remaining.

Information from the Soviet Union on Flamingo numbers and distribution is not very complete, but there is a long-standing breeding population at Lake Tengiz in the Kirghiz Steppe of Kazakhstan. In the mid-1940s, it is said that about 25,000 pairs bred around the north-east part of the Caspian, but disappeared when the area silted up. It is not known whether any were breeding at Lake Tengiz at that time, but the population there now is put at around 10,000 pairs. This total suggests that Gorgan Bay in the south-east corner of the Caspian cannot be the only wintering site for this population, others perhaps existing in the Russian part of the Caspian. Recoveries of birds ringed in the USSR, particularly at Lake Tengiz, give a scattering very similar to those ringed in Iran, but with the addition of two as far west as Tunisia; again young birds dispersing widely.

Afghanistan has been known as a breeding place for the Greater Flamingo since about 1946, though there are many earlier records of sightings. Breeding has been proved at two different lakes in the south-eastern part of the country, only some 150 kilometres (90 miles) from the Pakistan border. At Lake Ab-e-Istada, about 150 kilometres south-west of Kabul and 2100 metres (7000 feet) above sea level, breeding was proved in 1946, empty nests from the previous year were found in 1958, and between 500 and 1000 eggs and young were seen in 1966. Then in 1969, breeding was proved at Lake Dasht-e-Nawar, about 100 kilometres (60 miles) south of the other site and lying at an altitude of 3100 metres (10,000 feet). Some 6000 birds were involved, though there is no estimate of the number of nests. Both nesting sites are thought to freeze over completely in the winter and the birds probably migrate to Pakistan.

In Pakistan there has been just a single known attempt at breeding, at Lake Kharrar Jheel in the Punjab in 1966. A few hundred birds winter here, probably from Afghanistan, and at Saltrange Lake. In the Sind, in southern Pakistan, Flamingos are more common in winter, almost certainly birds from the Indian breeding site in the Rann of Kutch.

It was not until 1945 that Greater Flamingos were proved to breed in the Rann of Kutch, when the distinguished Indian ornithologist, Salim Ali, penetrated across the great sand desert to the coastal marshes beyond and there found a massive concentration of at least 200,000 nesting birds. After reaching the marshes, Salim Ali and his companions had to wade for three hours through ankle to thigh-deep brine. When they eventually reached the colony, they estimated that it covered an area of about 440 by 225 metres (actually 480 yards by 247 yards). They counted the number of nests in some sample plots of 100 square yards (c.84 square metres), then allowing for some bare areas within the colony, calculated a total of 209,516 adults. They estimated that there was a chick or an egg in two out of every three nests, or 69,839, to give a total of 279,355 Flamingos!

The Rann of Kutch had been known to hold very large numbers of Flamingos for a great many years, and breeding had long been suspected before Salim Ali's successful visit in 1945. Even after his discovery, though, the area has remained so extremely difficult of access that there are very few definite records of breeding since. Even though ornithologists have been there and found evidence of breeding, chicks or used nests, the timing of breeding is not at the same time each year so it is a matter of luck to arrive, as Salim Ali did in 1945, when the great majority of the birds were on eggs or with small young.

One of the few other years when there was a good count was in 1960, when there were at least 200,000 nests, or twice as many in 1960, and indicative of at least half a million Flamingos all told. Since then, however, a few tens of thousands of nests are the most that have been found, though this is not to say that larger colonies may not have occurred.

A small number of young birds have been ringed in the Rann. Salim Ali has written of the difficulties of chasing individual young Flamingos over the salt-flats, only to fall flat on his bottom, or to grovel in the mud, getting a perfect worm's-eye view of the young Flamingo making good its escape. The only consolation he found from this predicament was that on rising to his feet he saw that all his helpers were having similar problems!

Breeding has also occurred at the Thol Lake Sanctuary near Ahredabad, where about 5000-6000 birds were seen in June 1981, though only 70–80 nests and young were found. In 1977, several thousand Flamingos turned up at Lake Sambhar, which lies not very far from Delhi and nearly 500 kilometres (300 miles) from the Rann of Kutch. The lake is normally very saline, with little animal life in it. Then in the early 1970's a series of floods greatly reduced the salinity, and as it declined so the invertebrate life flourished. In some mysterious way the Flamingos, which hitherto had been merely casual visitors, learnt of these excellent conditions and moved in. By November 1982 not less than half a million birds were present, nearly all Greaters, though including some Lessers. Large numbers were also seen at two nearby lakes.

No breeding has yet been reported from Lake Sambhar but it must be considered likely if the birds stay there. However, in early 1984, large numbers of Flamingos were found on various wetlands in the Saurashtra area a little way south of the Rann of Kutch, and so maybe the Sambhar birds had moved back nearer their regular breeding haunt. Tbere was no certain breeding in the Rann of Kutch in the early 1980s, despite aerial surveys to

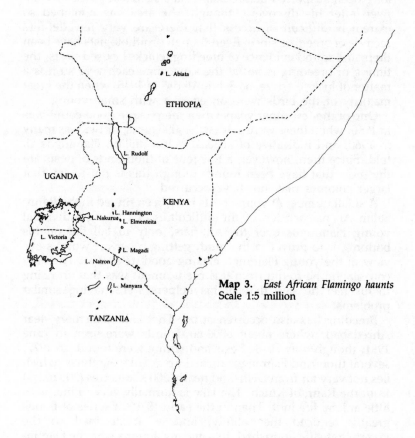

Map 3. *East African Flamingo haunts*
Scale 1:5 million

check on them, yet small numbers of juvenile Greaters were seen on the coast to the south in early 1984. There is indeed much still to be learnt about this population.

Apparently separate populations of Greater Flamingos occur in East and South-west Africa, though it is quite possible that birds may move between the two areas. In the Rift Valley lakes of East Africa, the Greater Flamingo is vastly out-numbered by the Lesser, but nevertheless there are an estimated 50,000 birds in the area. The two recoveries of Iranian-ringed birds in Ethiopia mentioned above suggest a possible connection with other groups, but this is likely to be very slight and restricted to wandering juveniles.

The first recorded breeding of the Greater Flamingo in East Africa was in 1903 when Colonel Richard Meinertzhagen found both Greater and Lesser Flamingos breeding on Lakes Nakuru and Elmenteita. He states that he ate some eggs, 'their orange-red yolks looking very appetising when scrambled in a pan with some fat', but did not see any young. He found them breeding at Lake Nakuru again in 1915, and in 1936, at the same lake, a self-styled 'sports-lady' fired into a large flock of flightless young Greater Flamingos, killing 22 and wounding many more. It can be assumed that they bred far more frequently than this, but there were very few naturalists in those days to observe them, particularly on the large, remote lakes which they selected.

The next authentic case of nesting was in 1951, when breeding again occurred at Lake Elmenteita. Details are incomplete but it is thought that about 1000 pairs were involved, and at least 500 young were reared. Since then, careful observations by, particularly, Leslie Brown have established that Greater Flamingos are quite regular breeders in East Africa, most usually on Lakes Elmenteita or Nakuru, or less often on Lakes Natron and Magadi, two pairs of adjacent lakes lying about 200 kilometres (125 miles) apart in the Rift Valley. Lake Natron lies in Tanzania, the other three in Kenya. All four are highly alkaline, and the breeding colonies are always placed far out on the great expanses of soda mudflats which appear when the water-level drops.

Breeding occurs on average every other year, but may take place in several consecutive years separated by a run of years without any attempts. In at least some years breeding has been prevented by high water-levels, but this does not explain all the gaps. The number of pairs has varied between about 500 and over 15,000, with an average of over 4000. There seems to be little connection between the birds of Lakes Elmenteita/Nakuru and Lakes Natron/Magadi, with in some years large numbers breeding at both sites, though whether the two groups are completely discrete is not known. It seems unlikely in view of the amount of movement of Lesser Flamingos between the same two groups of lakes (see below).

Away from the breeding sites, Greater Flamingos seem to be confined to the Rift Valley, visiting other lakes in both small and large flocks. Apart from the possibility of movement of young birds from Iran south through Ethiopia to Kenya, mentioned above, there appears to be no proven connection with any other population. There are a few records from Zambia which could be of birds from either East Africa or from Botswana, or possibly moving between the two areas. Only large-scale ringing will sort out whether or not there are connections between the different groups, but as there is certainly some evidence for movement of Lesser Flamingos between East Africa and Botswana/Namibia (see below) it would certainly be rash to dismiss the possibility that Greater Flamingos might also make the journey.

Breeding has only very recently been proved in Botswana, with the discovery in 1978 of a colony of 17,000 pairs at Makgadikgadi Pan. Flamingos have long been known to occur in considerable numbers in the area but as with so many sites it is one thing seeing the birds, quite another proving that they are breeding. There is a proven connection between the birds in Botswana and those in Namibia to the west, and so it is possible that breeding in Botswana is in fact quite rare, perhaps linked with years of failure or non-breeding in Namibia. As with very many matters concerning Flamingos, these questions will only be answered by more intensive observations, which the habits of the Flamingos do so much to thwart.

The breeding site in Namibia is at Etosha Pan, a vast and inhospitable saline depression over 6000 square kilometres (2300 square miles) in extent. It consists mainly of barren mudflats subject to irregular flooding. Breeding of both Greater and Lesser Flamingos was first recorded there in 1957, though may well have been taking place for a long time before that. In 1963, some unfledged young were found, while the following year abandoned nests and eggs were discovered. Breeding also occurred in 1968 and 1969 though there are no details.

In 1971, a more thorough study was carried out, including aerial surveys. These established that there was a cluster of 7 colonies spread over one area of about 2 x 3 kilometres (1.3 x 1.8 miles) in the south-east corner of the Pan, with some 22,000 adults present, plus an eighth colony with 5000 adults about 20 kilometres (12.5 miles) away near the north shore. Thus some 27,000 Greater Flamingos were engaged in breeding that year, out of an estimated 50,000 to 100,000 birds present on the Pan. It was not possible to get a more accurate count because of the simultaneous presence of about one million Lesser Flamingos. Breeding has occurred several times at Etosha Pan since 1971, but accurate counts have not been made as frequently, though there were 5000 pairs breeding in 1978.

When Etosha Pan is dry, the Flamingos move to the coast of Namibia, round Walvis Bay and Sandwich Harbour, about 500 kilometres (310 miles) away. When the rains come to the Pan, the birds leave the coast and fly back inland, though how they tell that the Pan is wet enough for them remains a mystery.

There have been a number of scattered attempts at breeding in South Africa. Numbers of birds are generally small, and it is thought that they are probably part of the same population as those in Namibia. In the 1950s, small numbers of nests were built in almost dried-up dams in the Orange Free State. The dams are built to hold water being pumped out of gold mines in the area. The water is quite saline and evaporation in the dams increases the salinity, thus providing the preferred habitat of the Flamingos. Although eggs were found on one or two occasions, no successful breeding has been reported from the area. Counts of birds on the dams have varied between nil and 4000, suggesting quite a lot of movement taking place.

In 1960, breeding took place in the Bredasdorp District of Cape Province, about 150 kilometres (93 miles) from Cape Town on the extreme southern tip of the continent. Two small colonies were established in an area that had been inundated five years previously by exceptionally heavy rains. Gradual seepage and evaporation had both dried up much of the area and produced strongly alkaline water and mudflats. It is thought that at least 800 eggs were laid, though there were probably considerably more than 1600 adults present.

The following year, 120 nests were established but heavy predation prevented any eggs hatching. At the same time 64 nests were constructed in the Rondevlei Bird Sanctuary close to Cape Town, but no eggs were laid. There was a more successful attempt in the Bredasdorp area again in 1963, when about 50 young were hatched. Further north in Cape Province, over 700 unfledged chicks were seen in February 1978 at Van Wycksvlei.

Greater Flamingos may have bred, or at least tried to, in the Transvaal in 1970–71, while there was a large-scale and successful attempt in Natal in 1972. Over 6000 nests were built at Lake St Lucia, a large saline lagoon on the coast north of Durban, and some 4000 young were reared. There have been a number of other breeding attempts in different parts of South Africa, showing that same lack of pattern and consistency so

Dawn in the Great Rift Valley

typical of Flamingos elsewhere, compounded by the large areas involved and remoteness of the chosen sites.

Small numbers of Greater Flamingos have been seen from time to time on the island of Madagascar, mainly at lakes on the west coast. Most records are of one or two birds, but over 40 were present on one occasion. There are also records of stragglers on the Aldabra atoll some distance to the north of Madagascar. The origin of these birds remains a matter for speculation, with South Africa as likely as Kenya.

The overall total of Greater Flamingos in the world is almost impossible to arrive at, mainly because of the lack of counts from India. Though there may well have been about half a million there in 1960, this is not a true guide to how many there might be now. If we take half of this figure, and add in the approximate totals for the other parts of the range, we get a figure of around 750,000, but it might be more, or it could be less!

Lesser Flamingo

Description and identification (see Plates 3 and 4)

This is the smallest of the six kinds of Flamingo, though size is not always easy to estimate when looking at distant birds. There is not a great deal of difference between the sexes, with the males just over a metre tall (just over 3 feet) when standing, the females just under a metre. This compares with the 1.6 metres (5 feet) of the largest Greater Flamingos, the only species with which the Lesser is found in the wild. Thus when standing together in a mixed group the bodies of the Lesser Flamingos will be seen underneath the bodies of the Greaters. The size of birds at a distance, however, without any comparisons, can be quite hard to estimate. Furthermore there is just a slight overlap in size between the smallest immature Greaters and the largest Lessers. So while a small Flamingo is very probably a Lesser, it is necessary to check its colour and bill pattern to be quite sure.

The adult Lesser Flamingo is generally a darker pink all over than the Greater, particularly on the head and neck, though as with all Flamingos the precise colour depends on its diet, and escaped birds from zoos can be very pale. The back and wings are mottled with deep crimson rather than scarlet, but the pattern of black outer halves and trailing edges to the wings, with the fore part red and pink, is similar to the Greater's. The bill, apart from a black tip, is dark red, and this colour extends back to an area around the eye, appearing almost black at any distance and giving the bird a distinctive heavy-billed appearance. Close to, the dark eye patch makes the bird's expression seem quite fierce. Even if size cannot be estimated accurately the very dark bill should always enable an adult Lesser Flamingo to be identified. The legs are dark grey, and thus also darker than in other kinds.

The downy young Lesser Flamingo is more variable in colour than the Greater Flamingo chick, ranging from almost white to dark grey. Its bill is blackish, while its legs and feet start off red but quickly darken to blackish. The juvenile Lesser Flamingo is not easy to separate from the Greater Flamingo young, but is overall a little darker, being browner on the head and neck and less pale underneath. The bill is noticeably darker from an early age. As in other Flamingos there is a gradual acquisition of adult plumage over two to three years. The brown on the head is the last sign of immaturity to be lost but birds have actually been known to breed in that plumage, when perhaps three or four years old.

The voice of the Lesser Flamingo is distinct from that of the Greater, being much higher-pitched, though a flock in the distance is not so easily identified, as the calls merge together into a noisy chorus. The individual call is a yelping 'kwirrick', not at all like the deep goose-like honk of the Greater. There are a variety of other calls associated with display and breeding, again mostly high-pitched.

Feeding Lesser Flamingos tend to swing their heads and necks from side to side in a pronounced scything movement, with the bill only partly submerged. Greater Flamingos usually feed with their heads completely submerged, and often much of their necks, too. While not an infallible method of separating the two species, observing how the birds are feeding can provide additional clues to their identity.

Distribution and numbers (see Maps 3 and 4)

The Lesser Flamingo is confined to Africa south of the Sahara, where it is extremely numerous, and to India, where it is relatively uncommon. In Africa, the main concentration is found in the Rift Valley, in Kenya and Tanzania, with substantial numbers also in Botswana and Namibia. It seems quite likely that there is movement between these two areas, at least occasionally. There is a very small population in the extreme west of Africa, in Mauritania, and again there is the possibility of movement between here and East Africa. Finally, the Lesser Flamingo is seen more or less regularly in the southern Red Sea, the Persian Gulf, and north-western India, where there are also occasional breeding records, and it is thought that irregular movement from East Africa to India may occur.

The Lesser Flamingo occupies very similar habitat to the Greater Flamingo. Indeed, over virtually the whole of its range the two species are found together, on the same alkaline and salt-lakes and coastal lagoons, breeding on extensive mudflats. The main separation between the two species concerns their food and feeding habits. These enable them to exploit different foods within the same habitat, so that apparently mixed feeding flocks are in fact not competing for the same food supply. This will be dealt with in more detail in Chapter 5.

The Lesser Flamingo is undoubtedly the most numerous of the six Flamingos, but that is not to say that it is possible to put an accurate figure on the population total. Partly because it is so numerous, estimates of numbers vary enormously. There are certainly between three and four million birds in the world, but it is possible that there are as many as six million. The difficulty of estimating overall numbers is compounded by the extensive movements which vast numbers of birds may undertake in response to adverse conditions.

The Lesser Flamingo has been studied most in East Africa, on the soda-lakes in the Rift Valley in Kenya and Tanzania. Here Leslie Brown discovered the breeding grounds at Lake Natron in northern Tanzania. Although the vast flocks of Lesser Flamin-

Map 4. *Lesser Flamingo distribution*

Breeding sites ● + number

1. Mauritania
2. Rann of Kutch
3. Lake Abiata
4. Lake Rudolf
5. Lake Hannington
6. Lakes Elmenteita and Nakuru
7. Lakes Natron and Magadi
8. Lake Manyara
9. Lake Rukwa
10. Lake Mweru
11. Makarikari Pan
12. Etosha Pan
13. Orange Free State

Other haunts ▲

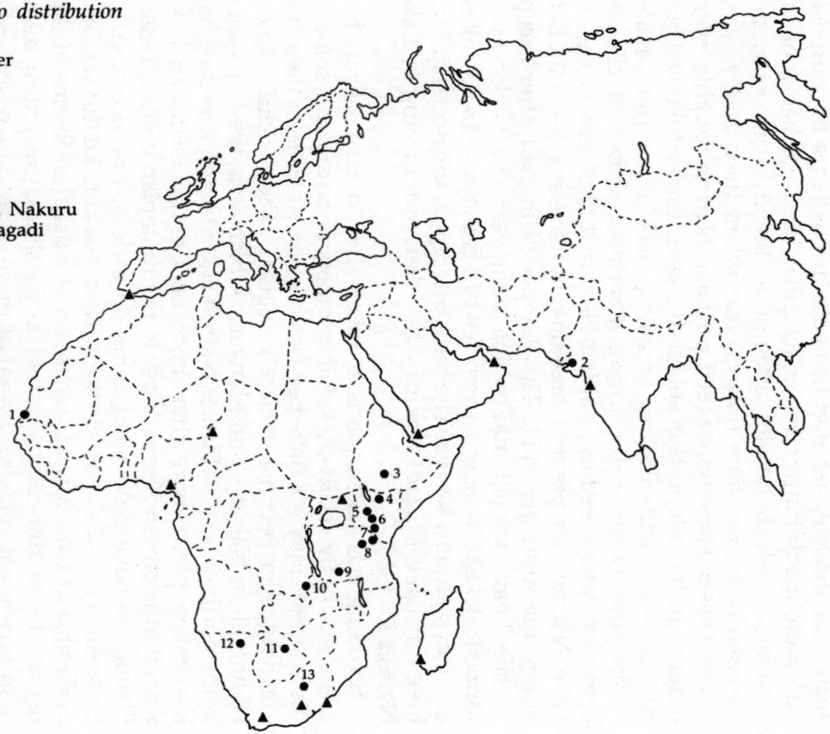

gos in East Africa were very familiar to people living there, and on the list of wildlife spectacles not to be missed of every visitor, it was not until 1954 that Leslie Brown finally pinned down where they bred. It took him several years of persistent searching, made easier after he had learnt to fly for the purpose, but made much harder by the irregular breeding habits of the Flamingos, which do not attempt to breed every year, nor necessarily at the same time of year when they do try.

The Lesser Flamingos breed on Lake Natron roughly every other year, but attempts in successive years can be followed by a run of years without any breeding, just as in the Greater Flamingos. There is no strong association between climatic conditions and breeding, but it is clear that high water-levels in Lake Natron can prevent breeding by covering the mudflats where the nests are built. This happened in 1961 after exceptionally heavy rainfall, and the following year a vast colony was formed at Lake Magadi, some 30–40 kilometres (18–25 miles) away in southern Kenya. The birds attempted unsuccessfully to breed at Lake Magadi again in 1963 before returning to Lake Natron in 1965.

Breeding has taken place at other sites in East Africa, but usually only by relatively small numbers of birds, and some of the attempts may not have been successful. At none of them has breeding ever become remotely regular. They include Lakes Hannington, Nakuru, and Manyara, which lie in the Rift Valley to the north or south of Lakes Natron and Magadi. Breeding has also taken place more than once on Central Island in Lake Rudolf in northern Kenya, close to the Ethiopian border. Lesser Flamingos have bred in Ethiopia on at least one occasion, at Lake Abiata, and also in southern Tanzania at Lake Rukwa, and in Zambia at Lake Mweru. There are the usual problems in this region of size, difficulty of access, and politics, preventing more than occasional visits to several of these lakes, when, as Leslie Brown found, only persistent searches over a prolonged period will pin down precisely what the birds are doing.

The same problems have hindered accurate assessments of numbers, compounded by the sheer difficulty of counting or even estimating just how many birds there are in huge flocks or nesting colonies. When Leslie Brown started looking at the Lesser Flamingos in the 1950s he found a vast concentration at Lake Hannington which he, and an independent observer, estimated at around two million birds. When he proved that breeding was taking place at Lake Natron he made flights over the colony to estimate numbers, and thought that in 1957 there were in excess of half a million breeding pairs.

Counting or even guessing at numbers of this magnitude is open to all sorts of errors, as Leslie Brown was very willing to admit. When, in 1962, the largest nesting colony ever was formed at Lake Magadi, he and his co-worker Alan Root were at pains to make as accurate estimates as they could. They used two different methods which, pleasingly, gave very similar results. Firstly, Leslie Brown flew over the colony and, using his experience from counting the colonies at Lake Natron in previous years, estimated that it occupied around 1.33 million square metres (1.6 million square yards). Within this area there were clumps of nests, at about four nests per square metre, but also considerable areas, estimated at 85% of the total colony, without any nests. The number of nests worked out at 960,000. In addition there were a further 120,000 nests in three smaller outlying groups, giving a grand total of 1,100,000.

Alan Root used a different method for his estimate. He worked on the ground, pacing out the size of the colony, making it slightly larger than Leslie Brown at 1.4 million square metres. Then he counted the number of nests within no less than 96 sample plots each of 100 square yards (84 square metres). With this figure, which averaged 55, he came up with a total for the main colony of 935,000, plus 100,000 in the outlying colonies. The closeness of agreement with Leslie Brown's estimate gave added credence to the latter's aerial counts of the Lake Natron colonies.

There have been other counts of the Lesser Flamingos in more recent years, including aerial surveys designed to find all the birds within the Rift Valley. These have usually been a mixture of actual counting plus aerial photography, the latter often sampling flocks, rather than attempting total coverage. The difficulties involved can be illustrated by what happened at Lake Natron in 1958, when two biologists carried out aerial photography of a considerable part of the lake and its mudflats, and then counted the birds on the photographs. They came up with a total of 163,679 and from this doubted Leslie Brown's estimate of a million or more birds on the same lake a year or two earlier. When they published the map of the lake showing exactly which parts they had photographed, Leslie Brown was able to show that they had missed out the central sodaflats on which half a million or more Flamingos were at that very time breeding!

In March 1969, an aerial survey found just over 1,100,000 Flamingos in the Rift Valley, covering virtually every important lake in the area. It was not possible to distinguish Greaters from Lessers, either directly from the air or from the photographs which were taken, but it can be supposed that there were no more than the previously estimated 50,000 Greaters present, the rest being Lessers. In the mid-1970s, a series of aerial surveys found no more than half a million Lesser Flamingos in the same area. However, although these surveys were almost certainly much more accurate than some of Leslie Brown's pioneering efforts, they were not in themselves evidence that the population had crashed dramatically.

The first point which emerged from the surveys was that Leslie Brown probably had over-estimated the total population. When he had found very large concentrations, as he did on a number of lakes in the course of his several years of intermittent study, he assumed that rather more of them were different individuals than has subsequently turned out to be the case, once it became possible to look at all the lakes over a fairly short period of time. It is now known that over 90% of the East African population can assemble on one lake simultaneously, as has occurred a number of times at Lake Natron, as well as at Lakes Nakuru and Hannington.

The largest single count of Lesser Flamingos remains Leslie Brown's and Alan Root's nest estimate at Lake Magadi in 1962, which indicated that about two and a quarter million birds were breeding there. What is not known, though, is how many Flamingos were on other lakes at the same time. Modern evidence suggests rather few, whereas at the time Leslie Brown thought there could easily have been a further one to two million.

There were undoubtedly fewer birds present in 1969 than there had been in 1962, and this drop was not readily explained. However, the mid-1970s surveys, which only found half a million birds, also led to the suggestion that there was movement from East Africa to Botswana and Namibia, which had previously been discounted. In early 1974, there was a count of about 1.4 million Flamingos on Lake Nakuru. Then the algae on which the birds were feeding virtually disappeared, probably because of changes in water-level and salinity in the lake. Numbers of Flamingos declined rapidly, but the aerial surveys in late 1974 and subsequently failed to find them within the Rift Valley as had been expected. Instead, there was a report of an enormous concentration, estimated at about one million birds, on the Makarikari Pan in Botswana. There were very few previous estimates from the Pan, but it did seem more than a coincidence that this enormous number should be present at a time when numbers were unusually low in East Africa.

Lesser Flamingos have bred recently at Makgadikgadi Pan,

Lesser Flamingos

near Makarikari, with some 800 nests among the very much larger Greater Flamingo colony that formed there in June 1978, but the main breeding location is in Namibia, at Etosha Pan, where the Greater Flamingos have also bred. Flamingos of one or both species are known to have bred at Etosha in a number of years since their discovery there in 1957, and presumably did so in many years prior to that. In 1969, at least 100,000 pairs bred and then suffered a near-disaster when rapidly dropping water-levels left tens of thousands of young chicks stranded. Very large numbers died of starvation, thirst, and predation before a rescue operation could be mounted during which 20,000 chicks were captured and transported across the Pan to an area which still held water.

In 1971, there were an estimated one million Lesser Flamingos present, and about 30,000 pairs bred in two areas, one containing seven colonies, the other a single colony. These were in the same places as the Greater Flamingo colonies already described, but the Lessers did not breed until after the Greaters had finished. Although the water-levels gradually dropped through the season, they had started at a higher level than in 1969, and there was no comparable die-off of young. Breeding has taken place at Etosha in a number of years since.

When Etosha Pan dries up, the Lesser Flamingos move, like the Greaters, to the Namibia coast, particularly to Walvis Bay and Sandwich Harbour. There is also some movement south into South Africa, but the Lesser is more thinly scattered there than the Greater, especially considering the vastly greater numbers in Namibia. There has been no record of mass breeding of Lessers in South Africa, though small groups have tried in a number of places. For example, there were 60 nests on a dam in the Orange Free State Goldfields in 1959, in the same area in which small numbers of Greaters have bred, but all the nests got flooded. Over 20 nests were built, though no eggs laid, in the Bredasdorp district near Cape Town in 1965, and there was a similar occurrence just outside Cape Town in 1972. In 1978, a few pairs bred on the Britten Salt Pan in the Transvaal.

There is some disagreement among biologists about the ability of Lesser Flamingos to move between East Africa and Botswana. Leslie Brown thought that Flamingos only flew long distances at night, and given their average flying speed of about 55 kilometres per hour (34 miles per hour), their maximum range of up to 640 kilometres (400 miles) was insufficient for them to fly the 1440 kilometres (900 miles) from their southernmost East African haunt at Lake Mweru in Zambia to the Makarikari Pan in Botswana. The distance from Makarikari to Etosha is 960 kilometres (600 miles), but there are one or two places in between where the birds could at least come down and rest if not actually find any food. There are apparently no such sites between Zambia and Botswana.

The contrary view states that Flamingos do not necessarily only fly at night. Although hardly any movements have been seen during the day, this could mean that the birds are flying too high to be seen readily from the ground; something which many migrating birds do. Furthermore, calculations of the amount of fat which Lesser Flamingos can store for use on a long migration suggest that a flight of 1500 kilometres (950 miles) is well within their capability. Rather few Lesser Flamingos have been ringed and so far there are no recoveries to support the view that they do make this journey.

Small numbers of Lesser Flamingos have occurred on Madagascar, paralleling the records there of Greater Flamingos. They have mostly been on coastal areas in the south-west of the island. In areas adjacent to Kenya and Tanzania, the Lesser Flamingo is not at all common. Up to 1000 were found on Lake Bagusa in western Uganda in spring 1969, an exceptional number for that country, but later in the year they had nearly all gone again. As well as occasional breeding records in Ethiopia, flocks are often present on lakes in the south of the country.

These may perhaps include birds moving to or from the Red Sea and further afield.

A really long flight would be needed for Lesser Flamingos to reach West Africa, yet there is a small population, breeding sporadically, on the lagoons of Aftout es Samel in southern Mauritania. They were first found breeding in 1965, when there were about 800–900 pairs, but may have been present for many years before that. Since then, breeding has not been proved again, but flocks of birds have been found among much larger numbers of Greater Flamingos on the mudflats of the Banc d'Arguin to the north. Over 3000 were counted there in 1973.

There are scattered records of quite large flocks elsewhere in West Africa, including 2000 on the Cameroon coast in 1932, and these, taken with occasional sightings on Lake Chad in the centre of the continent, do suggest a possible overland flight from East Africa. Certainly the breeding occurrences in Mauritania hardly seem enough to produce a self-sustaining population. What are presumably vagrants from West Africa have turned up in southern Spain on two occasions in recent years, both times associating with Greater Flamingos, and so perhaps confirming the link between the western Mediterranean and West Africa for the latter species, which ringing has demonstrated.

The Lesser Flamingos of north-west India and Pakistan are also a puzzle, because although it appears that there may be some tens of thousands of them, mainly in the Rann of Kutch among the very large flocks of Greater Flamingos there, breeding has only been proved once, in 1973 when up to 5000 bred there. If this population is maintaining its numbers, then either they are breeding more frequently, which is decidedly possible in view of the difficulties in getting to the breeding area let alone making comprehensive observations, or there is a more or less regular movement of birds to and from East Africa. The latter view is supported by the fairly regular sightings of birds in the southern Red Sea and in the Persian Gulf. On the other hand, in spring 1984 over 150 newly-fledged juveniles were seen among about 2000 Lessers along the shore of the Gulf of Kutch, yet aerial surveys had failed to find any breeding in the Rann in either of the two previous years. This suggests that there must be another, as yet undiscovered, breeding site in the area.

Chilean Flamingos

Chilean Flamingo

Description and identification (see Plates 4 and 5)

The Chilean Flamingo is most like the Greater Flamingo in size and colouring. It is slightly smaller, particularly in its length of leg, though other measurements, like wing-span, show a great degree of overlap. The adult Chilean is a very pale pink fading to white on the head, with long bright crimson feathers drooping over its back. When in full breeding plumage the lower neck and breast are tinged with a bright rosy suffusion. The legs are a dull yellow or yellowish-grey, with strongly contrasting bright pink joints and feet. The usual black tip on the bill extends back to just beyond the bend, the rest being whitish, or very pale pink. The iris is yellow. There is quite a lot of colour in the red forewing when the bird is in flight, though not quite as bright as in the Caribbean Flamingo. The downy young, juvenile, and immature plumages of the Chilean Flamingo are extremely similar to those of the Greater Flamingo.

In its native South America, the Chilean Flamingo can be distinguished fairly readily from the other two species there, the Andean and the James', by the lack of any yellow on the bill, the prominent reddish 'knee' joints, and the absence of any strong colouring on the head and upper neck. The red 'knees' are also the best way of identifying the species in captivity, when the very similar Greater Flamingo may also be present. The other good clues are the rosy colouring on the lower neck and breast, though this is only present in the breeding season, and the greater extent of black on the bill.

Map 5. *Chilean Flamingo distribution*

1. Lake Junin
2. Salar de Uyuni
3. Lake Colorada
4. Salar de Chalviri
5. Lake Pozuelos
6. Salar de Surire
7. Mar Chiquita
8. Las Colorados
9. Chubut
10. Puerto Natales

Other major haunts ▲

Distribution and numbers (see Maps 5 and 6)

Very much less is known about the detailed distribution and numbers of the three South American species than about the three kinds already dealt with. The Chilean is the most numerous and much the most widespread of the Flamingos in South America. It occurs from the highlands of central Peru to Tierra del Fuego in the extreme south of the sub-continent, a distance of over 4000 kilometres (2500 miles). While mainly found on high-altitude lakes, it also lives in the lowlands in some areas.

There is a concentration of breeding haunts on the salt-lakes of the high Andean altiplano of northern Chile and western Bolivia, just extending into the extreme south of Peru and the north-west corner of Argentina. They mostly lie between about 3500 and 4500 metres above sea level (12,000 – 15,000 feet), and some, such as Salar de Uyuni in Bolivia, are enormous, up to 80 kilometres (50 miles) across, with all the difficulties in making observations and obtaining information that that implies, even with the help of aircraft surveys. The position is compounded by the habit of all three species to nest together in some localities in mixed colonies.

Breeding sites in Peru include Lake Junin, where they nested in the 1970s and again in 1984. The Yaurihuiri Lakes and Lake Parinacochas are important haunts for non-breeding flocks. Small numbers of Chilean Flamingos stray down to the Pacific coast of Peru, where they can be seen in the Paracas National Park, not very far south of Lima. Lake Titicaca, on the Peru-Bolivia border, is another haunt where several thousand non-breeding birds are regular.

The largest flocks of Chilean Flamingos have been counted on various Bolivian lakes. There were 100,000 present on Lake Poopo in January 1972, and 75,000 there the following January. An important breeding site is Salar de Uyuni, where up to 4000 pairs bred in 1973, while a little further south, similar numbers have bred at Lake Loromayu, in the Eduardo Avaroa National Faunal Reserve. They have also bred at two other lakes in the Reserve, Lake Colorada, the main breeding site for James' Flamingo, and Lake Chalviri.

There are breeding records from northern Argentina, at Lake Pozeulos, and northern Chile, at Salar de Surire in the Lauca National Park. There are few details concerning numbers or frequency, however. There are also at least two breeding colonies in lower-lying areas of Argentina, on the east side of the Andes. The extensive salt-lake of Mar Chiquita, between

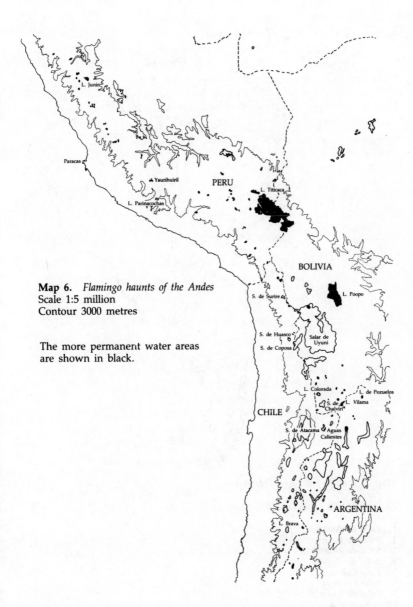

Map 6. *Flamingo haunts of the Andes*
Scale 1:5 million
Contour 3000 metres

The more permanent water areas
are shown in black.

Map 7. *Andean Flamingo distribution*

Breeding sites ● + number

1. Salar de Atacama
2. Salar de Surire
3. Salar de Huasco
4. Salar de Coposa
5. Lake Colorada
6. Lake Uru-uru
7. Salar de Chalviri
Other haunts ▲

Cordoba and Santa Fe, is home for up to 70,000 Chilean Flamingos. This number was counted quite recently, after a period in the 1970s when it appeared that the lake had been deserted. Between 5000 and 6000 pairs have bred there, too. Further south, in Patagonia, a colony of 3000–5000 pairs was found on a lake in Chubut Province in the early 1970s. Breeding has also been reported from one or two other lakes in the southern part of the Andes, both on the Argentinian side near Las Colorados, and on the Chilean side, at Puerto Natales, in the extreme south.

Various workers have attempted to make estimates of the number of Chilean Flamingos in South America, but all have suffered from the same major problems, the vastness of the range, the great remoteness of many of the haunts, and the difficulties in operating across national boundaries between states that are not always on the best of terms. The population has been put as high as one million, while in the mid-1970s it was assessed at about half a million. Recently, there have been estimates of perhaps 100,000 in Argentina, not more than 30,000 in Chile, and perhaps some tens of thousands in both Bolivia and Peru.

The approximate total from the above estimates of not much over 200,000 would appear to mean there has been a large decline, but maybe they are just rather more realistic figures. It is impossible to be certain how complete the estimates are, or how much overlap there is between the figures for the different countries. Certainly in the Altiplano area where Peru, Chile, Bolivia, and Argentina all meet, more or less simultaneous surveys would seem essential. The problem with this is that they have to be carried out from the air. Not only are some border areas rather sensitive for this sort of activity, but identifying the three species becomes much harder, and at times impossible. Clearly it is an unsatisfactory state of affairs, but very difficult to see how it can be overcome.

Andean Flamingo

Description and identification (see Plates 4 and 6)

This species is similar in size to the Chilean Flamingo, or perhaps a little larger. It often gives the impression of being a little more stoutly built, though this may owe as much to the colouring as to any genuine structural difference. The adult has its head, neck, and upper breast strongly tinged wine-red. This

Andean Flamingo

red breaks up into spotting on the lower breast against a
generally pale pink background which extends over the rest of
body. There are pinky-red feathers in the wings which show up
in flight, contrasting with the black outer feathers, and also
providing colour on the back of the standing bird. The bill is
yellow at the base, the outer half being black, and there is a
distinctive red spot between the two nostrils on the upper
mandible. The iris is an orange-brown, while the legs and feet
are yellow. The downy young and juvenile go through a similar
sequence of plumages as the other species.

The almost purplish-red colouring of the head and neck of the
Andean Flamingo distinguishes it from all the other kinds. The
James' Flamingo also has a yellow and black bill, but the bill, as
well as the bird, is smaller, and the black is much more restricted
in area, so even the juveniles can be separated once this pattern
has appeared. The yellow legs are also unique among Flamingos.

Distribution and numbers (see Maps 6 and 7)

The Andean Flamingo is restricted to a comparatively small
area of the Andean Altiplano in southern Peru, northern Chile,
western Bolivia, and north-western Argentina, roughly 800 by
500 kilometres in extent (500 x 300 miles). This overlaps almost
entirely with the range of James' Flamingo, and with the
northern part of the range of the Chilean, though the latter, as
already described, occurs all the way down to the southern tip
of South America, too.

The principal haunts are high altitude salt-lakes, as used by the Chilean Flamingo, and similarly lying between about 3500 and 4500 metres (12,000 to 15,000 feet). The principal, and perhaps the only regular, site where Andean Flamingos have been found breeding is at Salar de Atacoma in Chile. Other less regular sites have included the salt-lakes of Surire, Coposa, and Huasco, in Chile, together with Lake Colorada in south-western Bolivia. There were perhaps 2000 pairs at the last-named site in 1957, though as they were mixed with as many Chilean, exact numbers are impossible to assess. There is one breeding record from the east side of the Andes, near Tucuman in northern Argentina, where a small number of flightless young plus adults were seen walking down a dry river bed.

Among the largest concentrations of Andean Flamingos to have been counted are 18,000 on Lake Uru-uru, Bolivia, in December 1970, 5200 at Lake Chalviri, Bolivia, and 5000 at Salar de Surire, Chile. Some recent surveys of the main range have found a maximum of just under 7000 Andean Flamingos in parts of Peru and Chile, with a count a year later of about 3500 in Bolivia. Another recent estimate puts the population in Chile at between 4000 and 6000.

There is little information on movements of Andean Flamingos. Clearly, though, it goes on between lakes in the Altiplano as the birds respond to changing conditions of water-level, food, and nesting conditions. Although the range is much smaller in area the same problems occur in arriving at meaningful population estimates as they do for the Chilean Flamingo, and with no greater chance of finding an adequate solution. Just as with the Chilean Flamingo there is a great lack of information about even basic population levels, let alone any changes which might be taking place. Almost everyone who has worked on South American Flamingos in recent years, however, is concerned that there are indeed fewer than there were not many years previously.

To what extent those counted represent different birds or what fraction of the whole is not known. About ten years ago the total population of Andean Flamingos was estimated at about 150,000, though possibly as low as 50,000. A totally unsubstantiated estimate of half a million birds which was published in the late 1960s can be completely discounted.

It has been almost universally stated in the literature that the James' Flamingo is the rarest kind in the world, followed by the Caribbean. Evidence from surveys in South America over the last 15 years, incomplete though they have been, suggests that the Andean is possibly now the scarcest of all,

Map 8. *James' Flamingo distribution*

Breeding sites ● + number

1. Lake Colorada
2. Lake Poopo
3. Salar de Uyuni
4. Lake Chalviri
5. Lake Vilama
6. Salar de Surire
7. Aguas Calientes
8. Lagunas Brava

Other haunts ▲

with an absolute maximum of 50,000 individuals and probably many fewer.

James' Flamingo

Description and identification (see Plates 4 and 7)

This is the smallest of the three South American Flamingos, and only a very little larger than the Lesser Flamingo of Africa. It has whitish plumage delicately suffused with pink. The rose-red scapulars drooping over the black wings and tail are elongated with long, narrow tips. In full breeding plumage, there is a broad band of carmine spots on the breast. This is only rarely present in captive birds. The legs and feet are orange-red, while the bill is the most coloured of all the Flamingos. The tip is black and the inner two-thirds are an orangey-yellow. The latter is separated from the bird's face by a narrow carmine band which extends back to around the eye. In flight, all the main flight feathers are black, including those closest to the body which in the other kinds are red. The forewing is red as in the other Flamingos.

The downy young and immature stages have not been thoroughly studied, but it appears that they differ little from the other Flamingos, with mature adult plumage not being achieved for three or more years. The bill of the immature is certainly a duller yellow than in the adult, and the carmine band at the base is absent or very narrow.

Distribution and numbers (see Maps 6 and 8)

The distribution of James' Flamingo is the most restricted of any of the six kinds. Like the Andean Flamingo it is found on

James' Flamingos

the high Altiplano salt-lakes of the Andes, in the extreme south of Peru, western Bolivia, and northern Chile and Argentina. It does not extend so far south in either of the last-named countries as the Andean Flamingo, with the single exception of an extraordinary record of two individuals seen, and photographed, at a breeding colony of Chilean Flamingos in the Chubut Province of Argentina in 1973.

Chubut is approximately 2000 kilometres (1400 miles) south of the previously recorded southern limit of the species' range. It is difficult to assess the real significance of this observation. Assuming the James' were vagrants, they seem to have moved a very long distance. It is possible either that they became completely lost and linked up with the Chilean breeding colony by chance, or that there was a southward movement by the Chileans, from out of the James' normal range, and the James' got caught up in the movement. This, though, would suggest long-distance movements by Chilean Flamingos, which are certainly not usual.

The James' Flamingo's breeding haunts were not discovered until as recently as 1957. The major work on Flamingos by Robert Allen, published in 1956, included the then true statement that no actual breeding sites of the James' Flamingo had ever been seen or described. This was regarded as a direct challenge by A.W. Johnson, an ornithologist living in Chile, and later author of 'The Birds of Chile'. He collected together a small group of keen friends and set off on a five-week journey into the Andes of northern Chile. They travelled over 5000 kilometres (3000 miles) in a variety of vehicles, as well as on mules, visiting all the possible Flamingo haunts they could find in an area nearly 600 kilometres (400 miles) long and 200 kilometres (120 miles) wide.

At one point in their journeying they made a short diversion into south-western Bolivia to visit a salt-lake called Colorada, the Red Lake. Here, in January 1957, they saw a small number of James' Flamingos among many Chilean and Andean. Meeting a local Indian, they were told of two nesting colonies on islands far out in the lake, from which the Indians traditionally collected the Flamingo eggs for food and for sale. Johnson and his party persuaded the Indian to guide them to the colonies, after assuring him that they were not going to scare the birds away, or interfere with his egg-taking.

The account of the trek across the shallow lake to the colony islands is remarkably similar to those of other expeditions carried out to find Flamingo colonies on other continents, including Salim Ali's discovery of the Greater Flamingo colony in the Rann of Kutch, and Leslie Brown's close encounter with death in his pursuit of the Lesser Flamingo's breeding grounds. The first island proved to be well over a mile into the lake. The water was shallow, but every so often there were apparently bottomless holes out of which hot water bubbled from volcanic subterranean springs. Stretches of soft, slimy mud were interspersed with areas of hard salty crust, through which their feet often broke, gashing their ankles and legs on the sharp edges.

When they finally arrived at the island, apparently comprised entirely of salt, a colony of at least 2000 pairs of breeding Flamingos confronted them, and there, in among many Chilean and Andean, were a small number of James'. The next day they visited the second island and found not more than 20 to 25 pairs of James' among a further 1500 pairs of the other two species. There was no segregation between the three kinds.

The following year, other scientists visited Lake Colorada and found that the James' was then the commonest of the three species, with between 5000 and 7000 birds engaged in breeding. Again in 1960, up to 4000 birds were breeding there. More recently there have been counts of up to 26,000 James' Flamingo at this one lake, which remains by far the most important single site for the species.

Large numbers were reported breeding in 1968 at Lake Poopo, Bolivia, about 300 kilometres (220 miles) north of Lago Colorada, and breeding has also been reported from Salar de Uyuni not far away, as well as at Lake Chalviri close to Lake Colorada. In Argentina, James' Flamingo has nested at Lake Vilama, while in Chile, there was a possible breeding attempt at Salar de Uyuni in 1972 and also at Aguas Calientes and Lagunas Brava, the southernmost site for this species.

The total population of James' Flamingos has been put at between 30,000 and 50,000. The largest number seen together was the 26,000 at Lake Colorada, yet just a few years earlier there were only 20 present. This illustrates perfectly the difficulties facing anyone trying to arrive at a meaningful total, and makes assessing changes in overall numbers virtually impossible. Surveys in the mid-1970s found a total of over 10,000 in Chile and Bolivia in 1975, and over 12,500 in Bolivia alone in 1977. There are always a significant proportion of unidentified Flamingos in these surveys, so the true number of James' remains as yet unknown. What seems certain, though, is that this is not the rarest Flamingo as commonly thought, but at least equal to and quite possibly more numerous than the Andean.

CHAPTER 3

Behaviour

Flamingos are gregarious birds, occurring naturally in flocks, occasionally of just a few individuals, but more often in thousands, sometimes in tens of thousands or more. Whether feeding or nesting, they pack closely together, following the old adage about safety in numbers. Many species of birds are highly territorial, defending a small or large area around themselves and their nest against interference by others of their kind. Flamingos are far more tolerant than this and only indulge in a few quite mild threat displays to keep their actual nest-site sacrosanct. With their food of algae and invertebrates tending to occur in dense growths and swarms, this quite naturally leads to equally dense flocks of feeding birds, with little need for each bird to defend its own food supply against other Flamingos.

One of the more spectacular sights in the natural world is a flock of Flamingos indulging in group displays. Tight masses of birds march to and fro, or stand erect opening and closing their wings abruptly to flash red and black. It is thought that this behaviour is vitally necessary to the Flamingos in order to get as many birds as possible into the correct state for nesting at the same time.

Birds nesting in temperate latitudes with regular seasons of spring, summer, autumn, and winter, come into breeding condition regularly every spring. Thus they begin nesting at the same time as the plants and insects on which they feed themselves and their young are growing and multiplying. This pattern of regular breeding is normally triggered by hormone changes within the birds. These changes are themselves set off by the gradual increase in the daylength through the spring period.

In the sub-tropics and tropics, where the Flamingos mainly live, not only is the change in daylength between winter and summer much less, but if their hormones were triggered to bring them into breeding condition each spring there would be many years when they could not breed. This is because the climate of these areas is very fickle. At nearly all the known Flamingo nesting localities, the birds can only breed if there has been sufficient recent rainfall. This provides both the right conditions for nesting, with muddy islands surrounded by shallow water, as well as an abundance of food for the nesting birds and, later, their offspring.

The rainfall of the tropics and sub-tropics, however, is notoriously erratic in timing and quantity. It is therefore essential that the Flamingos are able quickly to take advantage of any favourable circumstances when they occur. In the absence of regular seasonal factors to bring their hormones into the correct physiological state for breeding, Flamingos need some other method of ensuring that large numbers of birds arrive at this stage simultaneously. The performance of the various displays by large groups of birds is believed to provide just that stimulation.

There are several different ritualised displays which the Flamingos use, both when in massed groups, as well as between the individuals making up a pair. Very often a sequence of displays is performed, one running into another as the level of intensity of display increases. At other times, a group of birds may carry out just one display over a prolonged period, presumably not reaching a sufficient pitch of intensity to move on to the next.

The different displays have been given names by researchers who have studied them, descriptive of what the birds are doing. Thus there is the 'head-flag', 'wing-salute', and 'twist-preen', as well as 'marching', and 'hooking'. Most of the displays seem to be performed by all six kinds of Flamingos, though there are often slight differences in the precise set of actions. It has been found that the closely related Flamingos, the Caribbean, the Greater, and the Chilean, perform displays which are more nearly alike than those performed by the other three kinds. Some of the displays have not been seen in one or other of Andean and James' Flamingo, though this may only be because these two have been less studied than the others, because of inaccessibility in the wild, and relative rarity in captivity.

Phil Kahl, who has studied all the different Flamingos in detail, has reviewed the various displays and display sequences and tried to standardise the names given to them, in order to reduce some of the confusion that has arisen between published descriptions. I will follow his nomenclature here, endeavouring to explain what each display looks like; nearly all of them can be seen very frequently in captive flocks. Phil Kahl's account, on which this is based, appeared in the book *Flamingos* (see Further Reading).

Alert Posture

This is more an attitude adopted by the birds than an actual piece of behaviour. It is most frequently seen when a group of Flamingos is suddenly disturbed. Normally, when standing, Flamingos hold their necks in an S-curve, with their heads no higher than the level of their backs. If they are asleep, their heads rest on their backs, with the bill-tip often tucked into the scapulars. On being disturbed, Flamingos shoot their necks straight up, their heads held as high as possible, though with their bills normally not above the horizontal. They may turn their heads from side to side, presumably searching for or keeping an eye on the cause of the disturbance. If a single bird suspects danger and stretches its neck upwards, others quickly follow suit, alerted by the first one.

Although not a display, as such, the 'alert posture' often leads into the 'head-flagging' display.

Head-flagging

When a group of Flamingos begins to display together they nearly always start off with 'head-flagging'. Sometimes they just stop there, break off the displaying and resume feeding or other activities, but just as often 'head-flagging' forms the first of a sequence of displays. It starts with a few birds among a loose

Chilean Flamingos wing-saluting

group of 20–30 or more lifting their heads into the 'alert posture', but usually with their bills pointing more upwards. They then turn their heads from side to side in a quite rhythmic and jerky fashion, once or twice a second, while at the same time calling loudly and continuously. As the display intensifies so the rate of flagging increases.

The different kinds of Flamingos have slightly different ways of 'head-flagging', with the Caribbean tending to hold its neck stretched straight up, while the Greater and the Chilean both have a slight bend in theirs. The Chilean also holds its bill more horizontally than either of the other two, and moves its head through a smaller arc. This display has never been observed in the Andean Flamingo, while the James' has its own quite distinct variation. Here the birds stand in a rough circle, all facing inwards, instead of in a cluster. Also, instead of stretching their necks up vertically, they stretch them out horizontally into the middle of the circle, with their bills pointing down to the water. Then they wag their heads from side to side, bending the neck to do so rather than rotating the head on the neck as the other Flamingos do. They simultaneously give voice to sharp, explosive calls.

Lesser Flamingos 'head-flag' like the Caribbean and Greater, but normally do it in a large, closely-packed bunch of birds, while at the same time indulging in 'marching' (see below).

Wing-salute

This is one of the more spectacular displays, and can frequently be seen in captive birds. All the six kinds of Flamingos perform this display, usually immediately following a bout of 'head-flagging'. Typically, a group will 'head-flag' for up to a minute, then suddenly change to the 'wing-salute'. Each bird ceases to 'head-flag' and then, with its head still held up and its neck out-stretched, spreads its brightly coloured scapulars, the long feathers drooping over its back, cocks its tail in the air, and flicks its wings open, holding them out to the side. This position is maintained for no more than a few seconds, normally 2–4, occasionally up to 10, before the bird as abruptly snaps its wings shut again, and proceeds to another display. As it 'wing-salutes', the bird ceases the loud calls it has been giving during the 'head-flagging', and instead makes only low grunting noises.

The effect of the 'wing-salute' display is dramatic: random flashes of black and red appearing suddenly against the overall background of pink. The opening and closing of the wings shows off to maximum advantage both the jet black of the main

Lesser Flamingo wing-saluting

wing feathers, and the brilliant colouring of the underwing
coverts and axillary feathers, which are normally almost
completely hidden.

There are some variations in this display as between the
different kinds of Flamingo, with the Caribbean and Greater
tending to hold their wings straight out to the side or even
behind their bodies, while the Chilean has them more in front.
The Chilean and the Caribbean both hold their heads pointing
upwards at about 45 degrees, but the Greater points its head
almost straight up, straining upwards to its greatest possible
height. The 'wing-salute' of the Andean and James' Flamingo is
rather different, with the wings slowly flapped to and fro once
or twice a second, instead of being opened and shut, though the
flashing effect is much the same.

Whether in a small group in a zoo enclosure, or among
thousands of birds on a salt-lake, there is no doubt that the
sudden flashing of black and red is a most eye-catching display,
made more so by the holding of the wings open for a few
seconds, so that the eye has time to register the sudden

appearance of colour and contrast before it as abruptly disappears again. As the display gains in intensity, so the time that the wings are held out decreases.

Inverted Wing-salute

This display appears to be most commonly performed by the females in a group of birds indulging in 'head-flagging' and 'wing-saluting', and is sometimes known as 'bowing'. The bird brings its neck down to the horizontal, cocks its tail high in the air, and then partly opens its wings over its back, with the tips pointing upwards. This gives a similar black and red flash lasting just one to two seconds before the bird closes its wings again. Andean and James' Flamingos have never been seen doing this display, but it is reasonably frequent in the other kinds.

The Greater, Lesser, and Caribbean Flamingos appear to carry out more or less identical 'inverted wing-salutes', but the Chilean does not stretch forward as it opens its wings. Instead the opened wings are brought up on either side of the upright head and neck.

Twist-preen

The sequence of 'head-flag' and 'wing-salute' is nearly always completed by a 'twist-preen'. One wing is lifted above the back a little and then slightly opened, allowing the primaries to droop down, exposing them as a black patch against the bird's side. At the same time the bird twists its head and neck round and gives the appearance of preening briefly behind the partly opened wing. It is not actually preening there, but, as happens quite frequently in bird displays, an action that was originally developed for preening, or some other movement with a useful function, has also been incorporated into a display. When preening, the bird keeps its head behind its wing for just so long as it takes to rearrange the feathers there, and its movements are smooth and slow. In the 'twist-preen', the head is never held behind the wing for more than a couple of seconds, and the whole action is jerky and quick.

The Lesser Flamingo varies this display by seeming to preen the feathers of the back while only very slightly lifting its wing, without lowering the black primaries. James' Flamingo apparently performs this display only very rarely, while it has not been recorded from the Andean.

Chilean Flamingos wing-leg stretching

Wing-leg Stretch

This, like the 'twist-preen', is a movement which normally has a useful function for the bird, and which has also been incorporated into a display. Stretching out one wing and the leg on the same side to the rear is common among birds, and appears to be analogous to stretching in humans, tightening up the muscles and tendons and then suddenly relaxing them, to give a beneficial feeling. Flamingos in a displaying group can often be seen doing this, but, like the 'twist-preen', more rapidly and jerkily than they would do in the normal way. It has only been observed in the Caribbean, Greater, and Chilean Flamingos, and appears to be more or less identical in all three. Chileans seem to perform it far more often than the other two, frequently preceded by 'head-flagging' and immediately followed by a 'twist-preen'. All the three kinds, as they perform it, emit a sound that has been likened to a 'satisfied sigh'.

Marching

The Lesser Flamingo is the finest performer of this display. It also occurs in the Caribbean, much less often in the Andean and James' Flamingo, and only very occasionally in the other two. Typically, it involves a large, dense group of birds, maybe numbering hundreds or even thousands. They pack into a tight mass, standing very upright, the breast of one practically resting on the back of the bird in front. Then they set off at a fast run,

CO

Marching and head-flagging display

abruptly reversing direction every so often. The neck feathers are raised and the under tail-coverts are spread, both contributing to a pinker appearance. The overall effect is to produce a darker pink mass of 'marching' birds moving to and fro within the general flock. The birds 'head-flag' almost continuously as they 'march'. All that can be seen from a distance is a forest of twinkling red legs and madly twitching heads below and above a solid wall of pink bodies.

The birds are packed so tightly together that other group displays, such as 'wing-salute' and 'twist-preen', cannot be performed. These are seen, though, from birds on the edge of the 'marching' group. Birds within the group may, as well as 'head-flagging', fence with their bills with immediately adjacent birds, flicking them from side to side, though not quite touching each other. They may also adopt the 'broken-neck' posture (see below). From time to time, pairs of Flamingos leave the 'marching' group and move away together, perhaps to carry out further displays to each other. Caribbean Flamingos, when performing a 'march', may suddenly slow down, stop, and dip their bills in the water as in 'false-feeding' display (see below), and then as abruptly resume their 'march'.

In one or two zoos in America and the Bahamas, Flamingos are crudely trained to rush to and fro in front of visitors in simulation of the 'march' display; a not very edifying spectacle.

False-feeding

As mentioned above, the Caribbean Flamingo may 'false-feed'

at intervals during its 'marching'. This, like the 'twist-preen' and 'wing-leg stretch', is using a perfectly normal, everyday action as part of a group display. The head goes down, the bill is submerged in the water, and typical feeding movements are made with the bill, though it seems doubtful that any actual feeding takes place. It is more as if some intervening action is needed between abrupt changes of direction by the 'marching' flock.

Broken-neck

A purely descriptive term, not an actual condition, the 'broken-neck' display seems to be confined to the Caribbean and, particularly, the Lesser Flamingos. In it, the neck is suddenly bent in two about the centre, allowing the head to drop down so that the tip of the bill rests on the feathers at the base of the neck. This most often occurs among 'marching' birds, and whilst in this position the bird may 'march' along for several seconds or even minutes. There is some relation between this display and the bird preening the feathers at the base of the neck, though during the display it is not thought that any actual preening takes place.

Hooking

This is an aggressive or threat display, carried out by all except the Andean and James' Flamingos. The bird extends its neck forwards at an angle of about 45 degrees, sometimes more, sometimes less. The head is held so that the bird appears to be staring at the ground, its bill strongly 'hooked' backwards and pointing towards its chest. The scapulars and back feathers are raised up and the bird then walks towards the object of its threat. This can be another Flamingo, but equally could be a predator. It is often linked with the next display.

Neck-swaying threat

The name for this piece of behaviour comes from the action performed by a Flamingo wishing to see off an encroaching bird, most usually when it is on its nest. It first adopts the 'hooking' threat and then, if this seems not to produce the desired result of an opponent retreating, begins to sway its head and neck to and fro. The swaying can take the neck nearly at right-angles on either side of the body. A better name for this display, though, might be the 'chrysanthemum', because as the bird sways its

Chilean Flamingos neck-swaying

neck, so it lifts and spreads the scapulars and back feathers into a red and pink rosette looking for all the world like a giant, multi-petalled flower.

'Neck-swaying' is carried out by all six kinds of Flamingo, and is usually accompanied by a series of low grunts. If the threatened bird does not immediately retreat, it, too, may adopt the same posture, and the two birds will display at each other, with their bill tips just not touching. When the display is at its most intense, the bills are held very slightly open. At this stage, an actual fight can begin, though this usually amounts only to some pecking at each other; actual damage is hardly ever done. Fighting is commonest when two pairs get too close to each other during the selection of nest-sites. Once a Flamingo is incubating on its nest, it is very rare for any approaching bird not to be driven off by the threat alone, particularly when reinforced by the off-duty mate.

Pairing displays

There is no very dramatic series of displays between the birds of a pair. The forming of a pair seems to take place very discreetly, probably by a male coming and standing close to a female while she is feeding. Then when he moves away, she will tend to follow him. Later, as they stand side by side, they will stretch their necks up and call softly. Other apparent pairing displays include 'false-feeding' and preening of the wing-coverts. These actions also occur in other situations, of course, but, if seen being carried out just by the birds of a pair, then it seems that they have some significance in forming and maintaining the pair-bond between them.

Pairs will apparently take part in group displays, before gradually moving away together. Copulation is not seen until this stage is reached. It is usually initiated by the female walking around, immediately followed by the male, who holds his head and neck stretched forward over her back in the 'hooking' display, sometimes even touching it with his bill. When the female stops, the male mounts her, using his outspread wings for balance, and placing his feet in her inner wing-joints. He dismounts forwards over her head. After copulation, the pair may call together, with heads outstretched.

Display Sequences

The best studied Flamingos are those which have proved easiest to keep and to breed in captivity, namely the Caribbean, the Greater, and the Chilean. Thus, as was mentioned a number of times in the preceding sections, their displays are better known than those of the other three kinds. Studies on them have included noting the regularity of occurrence of sequences of display, and how often individual displays or complete sequences may be repeated.

Pairing display; the male 'hooking' over the female's back

The normal way for birds to begin displaying is with bouts of 'head-flagging'. During such bouts, individual birds may quickly perform some other display, particularly 'wing-salute', but return at once to more flagging. As the intensity increases, the birds begin to develop more of a sequence of displays, and their calling gets louder. Several birds will start a sequence together, and the commonest one is 'wing-salute' – 'twist-preen' – 'inverted wing-salute' – 'twist-preen'. Such a sequence may contain several 'twist-preens', one after another, though the other components are rarely repeated.

The above sequence is very usual among Caribbean and Greater Flamingos. The Chilean Flamingo often mixes 'wing-leg stretch' with its 'head-flagging', sometimes performing it twice running. This is more common in this kind of Flamingo than in the other two. It is most usual during low intensity displaying, though the female Caribbean, but not the male, may perform it at times when the general activity has got more frenzied. The 'wing-leg stretch' is also quite often followed by a 'twist-preen'.

Both 'wing-leg stretch' and 'twist-preen' can take place to either side of the bird's body. Quite frequently, and especially in the Caribbean and Greater Flamingos, if one is followed by the other, then they take place to the same side, but if the same display is repeated, the bird may alternate the sides. The Chilean tends to keep to one side only, and it has been noticed that when a pair of Chileans are displaying to each other they tend to stand a little further apart than pairs of the other kinds, and to display more towards each other, rather than just displaying together.

These differences in the way the different kinds of Flamingo

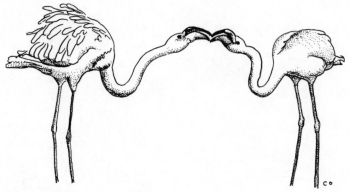

Greater Flamingos quarrelling

display are quite subtle, but are nevertheless real, and can be used to show that the Caribbean and Greater Flamingos are indeed slightly more closely related to each other than either is to the Chilean. The study of relationships between birds and animals does not have to depend solely on similarities of internal or external structure. It can just as well be based on how the birds behave.

To conclude this chapter, it is probably worth emphasising that the study of bird behaviour is not an exact science. While the current state of knowledge of Flamingo behaviour has been reflected here, particularly in relation to the terminology and descriptions of the different displays, it is by no means cut and dried, and further studies could well lead to changes in interpretation. In particular, more detailed studies in the wild could alter some of the conclusions drawn from observations on captive birds.

CHAPTER 4

Breeding

The breeding cycle of Flamingos, like much else about them, was not studied in detail until quite recently. Even now, this only really applies to the Caribbean and Greater Flamingos, and to some extent to the Lesser. The Chilean breeds well in captivity and much has been learnt about them in zoos, but the James' has yet to breed in captivity, and the Andean only has a few times. The remoteness of their breeding grounds in South America has precluded very detailed studies there. Past speculation on breeding habits has included supposed facts based largely on hearsay or a vivid imagination, and even now some of the myths persist.

Making allowances for the lack of information on some of the Flamingos, there are still many more similarities than differences in the breeding habits of the six kinds, and so this chapter will deal with the entire breeding cycle as common to them all, pointing out any variations that are known. It will cover from the selection of the colony site and the building of the nest to the fledging and maturing of the young.

We have already seen how the local conditions of, especially, rainfall and therefore water-level have an over-riding effect on whether or not Flamingos will breed at a particular time and use a particular site. There is a vital requirement for the presence of large areas of shallow water, either surrounding the colony site or immediately adjacent to it. In this way there is protection for the nests from ground predators, and an abundant food supply for the large numbers of birds often involved.

The really large colonies, for example of the Greater and Lesser Flamingos in Africa, and the Greater Flamingo in India, are situated on the exposed mud- or salt-flats forming part of the beds of enormous shallow salt-lakes and pans. Because of varying water-levels, the colony site will not necessarily be in the same part of the lake in different years. The beds of some lakes are so flat that a few centimetres change in water-level can produce vast differences in the area of standing water.

A second type of site frequently used is on small more or less permanent islands standing above the normal level of the water. For example, the best-known colony, that of the Greater Flamingos in the Camargue, is situated on just such a low island protruding no more than 20–30 cm (8–12 in) above the water of an artificial lake, or etang, used in the evaporation of sea-water for salt production. Over the years the island was gradually reduced in size and in height, having suffered from wave erosion, and from the years of nest-building which lowered its general level. However, it proved possible to drain the lake and to bulldoze a new island which the Flamingos immediately adopted. Further detail on this is included in Chapter 6.

In the South American salt-lakes, the Flamingos nest on islands of encrusted salt and rock, and in one of them, the Salar Uyuni in Bolivia, the islands are actually the tops of extinct volcanoes! Other rocky islands include those in Lake Elementeita, East Africa, and Lake Rezaiyeh, Iran, both used by Greater Flamingos. Some of the breeding attempts of the Greater Flamingo in South Africa have been at irrigation reservoirs. These have no suitable islands, so the Flamingos placed their nests on the low earth dams containing the water.

The mud- and salt-flats used for nesting are normally devoid of vegetation, or at most have a low covering of species such as *Salicornia*. Some sites, though, can have a much thicker growth of plants, including shrubs and low mangrove bushes. This does not seem to deter the birds, though they may pull up the plants or trample them underfoot.

One component of a colony site which has been thought to be vital, certainly when trying to persuade Flamingos to breed in captivity, has been the presence of plenty of mud of the right consistency for nest-building. However, although probably the majority of colonies are situated where there is such mud, many are not, particularly those on rocky islands.

A typical Flamingo nest is a conical mound of mud, about 30–40 centimetres (12–16 inches) high and 40–50 cm (16–20 in) in diameter at the base. This tapers to approximately 20 cm (8 in) across at the top, with a shallow depression inside no more than 2–4 cm (1–1½ in) deep. A number of used nests of Greater and Lesser Flamingos in Africa have been sliced off flat at the base with a spade and then weighed. The Greater Flamingo nests averaged about 52 kilogrammes (115 lbs) while those of the Lesser were around 30 kilos (72 lbs). The heaviest of both species topped a massive 80 kilos (180 lbs). It has been worked out that a colony of 250,000 pairs will excavate a total of around 7500 tons of mud!

As can be seen from the range of measurements given above, the size of the nest mound can vary enormously, depending no doubt on the amount of mud available to the birds. This variation is common to all six kinds of Flamingo, and so although the average measurements of their nests do differ a little, with the larger kinds making, on the whole, the larger nests, it is quite impossible to separate them on the basis of the measurements, the overlap is just too great.

The nest is normally built by one of the pair standing astride the nest-site and then, leaning down, carefully dragging the tip of its bill through the mud, pulling the mud towards itself and placing it between its legs. Depending on the consistency of the mud, this action may produce quite firm, rounded pellets, or merely a somewhat gooey liquid. The mud is then pressed into place with the bill and feet. As more material is incoroporated, so the nest begins to take on its familiar cone shape and the bird begins to stand on it instead of with a foot on either side. Often lumps of mud are dragged up the side walls, but then fall back down again. Many of these are abandoned by the bird and so gradually thicken and reinforce the base of the nest.

If there are harder objects, including small stones and pieces of vegetation, in the vicinity of the nest, these may get picked up in the bill and dropped into place. The bird turns slowly round as it builds, gradually clearing the surrounding area within its reach of debris and plant material, and, if the mud is soft, producing a series of adjacent pits which it has scooped out, or even a virtual moat around the growing nest.

There is quite a lot of variation in the pattern of nest-building, with the male often starting off, at least in captivity, and building in a desultory way for a few days or even weeks. Then the female, as she nears the point of egg-laying, takes over and may build quite fast and energetically for perhaps the last week. She often sits down on the job, scooping the mud towards her and tucking it up against her wings. Every so often she will stand up and walk about on the nest mound before sitting down in a different position. All this helps to firm the mud down and so ensure reasonably even building. Sometimes both birds will stand in the nest and build, though not actually helping each other. One of the pair may also stand beside the nest and pull material towards it, perhaps bringing it within reach of the building bird in the nest.

Quite usually the nest is still fairly low when the egg is laid, and this often seems to stimulate the birds into a frenzy of building. Nests can then grow from less than 10 cm high (4 in) when the egg was laid to more than 30 cm high (12 in) in only 48 hours. The birds pull the mud up the sides of the nest and on to the top, where it falls or flows down under the egg. This gets very muddy, as can be imagined, but seems not to come to any harm.

In hot climates the mud nest will bake hard under the sun and will then last many months or even years after use. Soon after building, however, when it is still soft, it can be very vulnerable to rain or to wave action. Incubating Flamingos have been seen apparently sheltering the nest from heavy rain by spreading their wings. And if the central depression fills with water they may suck this up into their bills and empty it out over the side of the nest. There is not much they can do against waves inundating the nesting island and its nests, and considerable losses can occur this way. A slowly rising water-level will lead to increased building activity, as the birds try to raise the nest-cup and its egg above the flood, but once the water starts to lap against the base of the nest, it is usually doomed.

Most of the above refers to the typical mud nest built when the colony is situated on a suitable soft surface. On hard rocky or salt islands, where there is no mud, the bird merely scrapes any available bits of debris, small stones, or rock flakes, towards itself, forming at best a small rim round a very slight depression in which the egg is laid. The most important function of the tall mud nest is to raise the egg safely above a possible rise in water level. This is vitally important on open mud-flats or low, muddy islands, but hardly matters at all on a rocky island already well above the water, so the lack of a tall nest in these circumstances is not a handicap.

Flamingos which return to precisely the same colony site in subsequent years will regularly refurbish old nests, patching them up, repairing rain or wave damage, and raising their height. In some colonies where space is very limited, successive groups of birds may breed on the same site, a new lot of breeders moving in as soon as the chicks of the first group have left. In one period of about 18 months, on Bonaire, Netherlands Antilles, the same colony site, and mostly the same nests, were used by the Caribbean Flamingos there no less than four times.

Within a colony, Flamingos' nests may be placed in dense clumps of many hundreds, scattered groups of half a dozen or more, or even in long lines following the cracks between polygons of hard soda. At their densest, Lesser Flamingo nests can be packed in at as many as 5 nests per square metre. The larger kinds are usually less closely spaced than this, with 1½ – 2 nests per square metre more normal. Incubating birds can spend quite a lot of time bickering with their neighbours, and so the closest distance between nests is generally just about two neck lengths!

Dense clumps and scattered nests can occur within a single colony. This may be related to patches of good building mud interspersed with harder areas. It is also possible that there may be sub-groups of birds, perhaps related, within the general breeding population, which nest closer to each other than they do to other similar sub-groups. On some small island colony sites nests will cover almost all the available space, and at high density. It is in the very large colonies on open mud-flats that the greatest variation in density probably occurs, where there is ample space for every pair.

Flamingos normally lay just one egg. A small percentage of nests in most colonies that have been studied have contained two eggs. For example, Etienne Gallet reported finding 40 nests with two eggs among 2000 which he examined in the Camargue. Leslie Brown found 5 clutches of two eggs among 900 Greater Flamingo nests in East Africa, and no more than 1 in 300–500 Lesser Flamingo nests. Similar percentages have been found in colonies of Flamingoes in India, South Africa, and the Caribbean. The question which remains, though, is whether the 2–egg clutches are laid by the same female.

There is no doubt that the normal clutch for a Flamingo is one. However, the female is known to be capable of laying a second egg if the first one is lost to a predator or a flood, after a gap of a few days. It is therefore physiologically possible for her to lay two eggs one after the other, though normally needing the stimulus of having lost the first egg. On the other hand, Leslie Brown found two eggs in a Greater Flamingo nest which were significantly different from each other in size and shape, indicating almost certainly that they had been laid by two different females.

Some authors have suggested that the second egg in some cases has been rolled into the nest, having fallen out of an adjacent one. This seems highly unlikely when the nests are the typical high mud cones, though conceivably it could happen in rocky island colonies where the nests are no more than slight depressions with a rim of debris. It is also possible for an egg to be laid in a nest already containing an unhatched egg left behind from a previous use of the nest, which can be only a matter of weeks before, as already mentioned. This could explain why some nests can contain a small chick, together with an unhatched egg. Alternatively it is possible that the chick had fallen out of one nest and climbed back into the wrong one!

Egg-laying has been most closely observed in captive Flamingos. Birds laying clutches containing several eggs frequently lay each one at roughly the same time of day, 24 or 48 hours apart. Flamingos, with their single egg, apparently lay at any time of day. The female comes to the nest and sits down, where she will remain for anything from a few minutes to an hour. Every so often she will shuffle and relax her wings a little, as if suffering from cramp. At the moment of laying, she drops her wings slightly and raises her rump but lowers her tail. Then she pushes her body forward until her breast is resting on the rim of the nest, and her neck on the side of the mound. After the egg has appeared, she will remain in this position for some minutes before getting to her feet. If she did not push her body forward as she laid the egg, there would be a danger of it going over the side of the nest mound.

The egg is off-white or tinged very pale blue when it is freshly laid. It is covered in a thick chalky deposit which very quickly becomes stained brown from the mud in the nest and from the parents' feet. The average size of the egg varies from 78 x 49 millimetres in the smaller kinds to about 90 x 55 mm in the larger ones (roughly 3 x just under 2 inches to $3\frac{1}{2}$ by just over 2). When fresh the smaller eggs weigh about 115 grams, the larger 140 (about 4 to 5 ounces).

Incubation begins as soon as the egg has been laid. Both sexes take turns in this, and the egg is never normally left uncovered. However, the incubating bird is often quite restless, standing up frequently, to stretch its legs and wings and to preen, and also to move the egg, pushing it around in the nest and turning it over. This is very important to ensure proper development of the embryo inside and is carried out by nearly all kinds of birds. As the bird sits down again it shuffles slightly from side to side

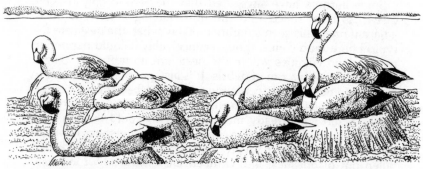

Chilean flamingos incubating

to bring the egg into close contact with its belly. There is no area of bare skin – a brood patch – as in many other birds, but the shuffling probably works the egg into the body feathers, closer to the warmth of the body.

Some fanciful ideas as to how Flamingos were able to incubate their eggs were put forward by early natural history writers unable to believe that the birds could bend their legs sufficiently. One theory was that the birds sat back on the nest mound with their legs in front as if perched on a stool. Another suggestion was that the legs were stretched out straight behind, while yet another had them dangling down either side of the nest. The truth is more prosaic. Flamingos sit down on their nests by folding their legs under them, the doubled 'knee' joints often showing to the rear.

The length of each incubation spell on the nest varies greatly, from well under an hour to 24 hours or even more. The really long periods seem to occur in colonies well away from suitable feeding areas, so that the off-duty bird has a long distance to travel to feed after it has been relieved. Leslie Brown found that in both the Greater and Lesser Flamingos nest-relief at night was very uncommon, and whichever bird was sitting as night fell sat through until at least dawn or after.

When nest-relief takes place, it is a very quick affair, without any of the elaborate ceremonies indulged in by some species. The incubating bird merely gets to its feet, stretches its wings, and then walks down off the nest, often flapping its wings and calling. Its mate then climbs up on to the nest from the opposite side, also flapping and calling, and in addition shaking its feet. This last action seems to have the purpose of removing any water from them which otherwise might get into the nest cup and soften the mud there. Sometimes the bird vacating the nest stops close by and preens itself, but as often it walks quickly out of the colony, and off to feed and bathe.

The egg hatches after about 28 days. This may vary a few days on either side, but seems to be about the same length of time in all six kinds of Flamingo. The young bird takes about 24 to 36 hours to come out of the egg after the first cracking of the shell appears. The adult gets very restless at this time, standing up much more frequently than usual, peering down at the egg, and gently touching it with its bill. The chick is now quite vocal, cheeping inside the shell, and being answered by its parents. In this way, they learn to know each other and will continue to recognise each other by voice during the rearing period, even from among hundreds or thousands of others in the colony. Once the chick has hatched, the eggshell often gets pushed over

the side of the nest, probably by the adult, but sometimes it gets crushed into the nest cup, and bits of it may get pecked at and even eaten by the chick.

The newly-hatched young is fairly weak to start with, recovering from the exertions of emerging from the egg. It cannot stand, but can raise its head and move around within the nest using its wings and breast. It pecks fairly indiscriminately at any tiny objects within the nest, including pieces of shell, small feathers, bits of mud, etc. Within a day or two, though, it is strong enough to stand on its legs, though often, and until it is many weeks old, it will sit on its haunches, with the lower legs and feet stretched out in front.

The parents brood the chick in the nest for quite long periods in the first few days. To start with they sit on it as if still incubating the egg, but soon the chick, presumably finding this rather uncomfortable, moves to one side until it is between its parent's body and one wing. It often then pokes its head out and looks around. It may call, and be answered by its parent, and it will also be fed while in this position.

The chick usually leaves the nest for the first time when it is between five and eight days old, though it can do so sooner, for example if the colony is disturbed. In the East African colonies, the temperature of the top of the nest was found to be many degrees cooler than that of the surrounding mud, 30–35 °C

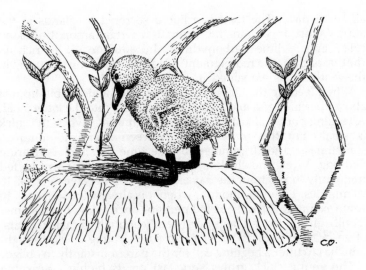

compared with 50–55°, which could be high enough to kill a very young chick. In these circumstances, premature exit from the nest might be lethal. By the time it leaves the nest the chick can walk and swim quite well, and indeed can probably swim very soon after hatching.

The parents stay close beside their chick, guiding it and calling all the while, and keeping other adults at bay with threatening movements of the head and bill. At intervals, they may return to their nest, whereupon the chick climbs up and is brooded there, but it may also climb aboard any convenient empty nest for brooding, or merely sit down where it happens to be. It seems that the act of sitting down on the part of the chick is a signal to the parents that it wants to be brooded.

As the chick grows older, so the parents leave it more and more in order to go and feed themselves. Large numbers of chicks will form into dense groups or creches, moving around together, gradually becoming more active and mobile. When an adult bird comes near the creche to feed its young, it calls, and is immediately answered by its own chick. This recognition works even when the creche numbers many thousands, and emphasises the importance of parents and chick learning each other's voice from the earliest moment.

Flamingo chicks are fed entirely by their parents for at least the first three to four weeks after hatching. They can certainly feed themselves by about 30 days old, but are still fed occasionally by their parents right up to the time of fledging, at about 75 days. The food is a liquid secreted by glands in the adults' crop. It contains fat, protein, a certain amount of blood cells, and a little carbohydrate. In addition, it is rich in canthaxanthin, the red pigment which provides the colouring in the feathers, as explained in Chapter 1.

When feeding the chick, the parent bird holds its bill tip just above the chick and allows the liquid to drip into the latter's bill. A feeding bout will last on average five minutes when the chick is small, but this increases to between 8 and 10 minutes, sometimes up to 20 minutes, by the time the chick is nearing fledging. While the chick is only a few days old it will be fed frequently throughout the day and night, on average every 45 to 90 minutes. Later on, though, when it is already feeding itself to some extent, it will only be fed perhaps once a day. By this time, it will only get fed if it begs persistently enough from its parents, often chasing them in order to do so. A young chick, though, only has to utter a begging call for the parent instantly to oblige.

The young chick grows very fast on its highly nourishing liquid diet. The first down coat is quite quickly changed for a second one, as explained in an earlier chapter. When it is about 30 days old, feathers begin to appear on the wings, and then the body. By about 50 days old, it is feathered all over, in the typical grey or grey-brown plumage. The bill, though straight to begin with, has a pronounced downward turn by the time the chick is about 40 days old. It is fully developed, and the chick is capable of proper filter-feeding, after roughly 70–80 days. This coincides

Feeding the chick

with the first flights, though for many days before that the chicks can be seen vigorously flapping their wings, exercising their muscles, and even performing power-assisted jumps into the air. The ages given here are for the larger Flamingos; the smaller ones usually achieve each stage a few days earlier.

Predation and floods have already been mentioned a number of times. There is almost always predation of some kind going on at a large Flamingo colony; it represents a very abundant food source for many carnivores. Nesting far out on dangerous mud-flats provides protection against many mammals, but if the water-level drops and the mud hardens, then obviously the colonies become vulnerable to hyenas or other animals. Foxes, otters, mongooses, and polecats have all been recorded as preying on Flamingo colonies to some degree.

However, the bulk of predation on Flamingo colonies is by birds. In East Africa, Maribou Storks have been found to be a major problem faced by Greater Flamingos. They not only eat many eggs and young, but cause incubating birds to desert in large numbers. In three years at Lake Elmenteita, Kenya, the Greater Flamingos lost over 12,000 chicks, or three-quarters of their total potential production, as a direct result of the Maribous.

Earlier observations of Maribous in Flamingo colonies had

indicated that they were not a major cause of egg or chick loss. The occasional Maribou would be seen walking through a colony, jabbing with its bill at incubating birds, but only infrequently would it be successful in obtaining an egg. More often, the Flamingo would rise up on its nest and lunge at the Maribou, causing it to back away. On one occasion, when a Maribou attacked a small creche of week-old young the Flamingo adults formed themselves into a solid phalanx and drove the stork off.

In 1968, at Lake Elmenteita, a maximum of no more than 17 Maribous contributed to a major breeding failure by some 4500 pairs of Greater Flamingos. The storks first arrived at one of the breeding islands, holding about 1100 pairs of Flamingos, just as the eggs were hatching. Storms and rising water-levels helped to make the Flamingos more nervous than usual, and in just four days the island was deserted by them. The Maribous then flew on to the next colony island causing panic and rapid abandonment by the Flamingos. This continued until the storks had visited almost all the 11 breeding islands.

In just one week, the combination of bad weather and the storks had caused virtually all the still-incubating Flamingos to give up, and had brought about the deaths of the great majority of the chicks which had already hatched. The Maribous only actually ate a comparatively small number of eggs and young, probably well under a hundred a day between them. Yet, having driven the adult Flamingos off an island, even though it was then littered with eggs and small young, the storks would move on to another island, as if the sight of the adult Flamingos was stimulating some aggressive instinct.

The pattern was repeated at Lake Elmenteita in 1969 and 1971. The Maribous again appeared on the nesting islands just as the eggs were hatching, causing consternation and panic among the adults, and rapid desertion of the islands. Some control of the Maribous has been possible since then, and it seems as if their population was in any case artificially higher than usual. Large numbers of storks had discovered a dump of offal from a fish factory nearby, and so there were many more within range of the Flamingo colonies than before. However, the factory closed in the early 1970s and many of the storks moved away.

Another, more surprising, cause of failure among breeding Greater Flamingos in East Africa has been Great White Pelicans. These birds have begun nesting among the Flamingos in recent years, breeding on the same islands. They are not overtly aggressive towards the Flamingos, and they certainly do not eat the eggs or young, but being much larger and heavier they have

just gradually taken over the space formerly used by the Flamingos. This also occurs at Etosha Pan in South West Africa.

In all parts of the Flamingos' range vultures and eagles take some eggs and chicks, though mainly abandoned ones, and various members of the crow family also scavenge around the edges of colonies. In South Africa, the Caracara, a large buzzard-sized relative of the falcons, is a regular predator on nests and chicks. Gulls can be even more of a nuisance, and this has particularly been the case in the Camargue. Here the Herring Gull has become a major predator, and as early as the 1950s it was estimated that as many as 1000 Flamingo chicks were being taken by them, or up to a third of the potential production in those years. More recently, however, the Herring Gulls have been learning how to take eggs, too.

Normally, an incubating Flamingo will not be too troubled by a gull, keeping it at a safe distance by lunging at it with its neck outstretched. However, the Camargue Herring Gulls have learnt two tricks for persuading a Flamingo to uncover its egg for the brief moment needed for a quick theft to take place. Firstly, they approach the incubating bird from behind and peck at its ankle joints. This makes the Flamingo stand up, whereupon the gull rushes forward and seizes the egg.

The second method is even cleverer. The Herring Gulls fly slowly over the colony virtually hovering into wind low over the incubating birds. Then as the Flamingos stretch up their heads to threaten them, a gull swoops lower, grasps one of them by the tip of its bill, and literally lifts it off its nest. It then lets go and drops down into the nest to grab the egg. Alternatively, another gull moves in instead. If there is no wind, the gulls walk around the very edge of the colony and attempt to pull incubating birds off their nest while themselves standing on the

ground. In recent years as many as 50 per cent of the eggs laid, amounting to several thousand each year, have been lost to the gulls.

Human predation is a major factor in some areas, particularly nowadays in South America, where Flamingo eggs are collected by the local Indians. There is plenty of evidence that a fairly low level of egg-collecting has continued for very many years, probably centuries, and it has also been reported from many other countries where Flamingos breed. Provided that it does not rise above this level, then there is unlikely to be a serious effect on the Flamingos.

Notwithstanding all the predators which Flamingos have to put up with, it is natural factors which dictate the success or otherwise of many of their breeding attempts. Storms, heavy rainfall, and the consequent floods have destroyed far more colonies than Maribou Storks. The opposite condition, the drying out of the mud-flats surrounding a colony, can be just as devastating. In the Etosha Pan in 1969, a rapid drying-up of the area caused thousands of chicks to die as they trekked up to 80 kilometres (50 miles) across the flats in search of water. In fact, long journeys by, particularly, Lesser Flamingo chicks are quite normal, it seems, but on this occasion the conditions were extreme and very many birds failed to survive.

At Lake Magadi, Kenya, in 1962, many tens of thousands of chicks died after thick rings of soda had formed round their legs. It happened when dense creches of chicks moved into areas where the very shallow water was completely saturated in soda salts, so much so that there was a thin film of crystals on the water surface. First of all a narrow ring collected round the birds' ankles, then over a period of days this grew into a ball the size of an apple. Impeded in this way the chicks became unable to walk properly, and succumbed in the glutinous mud.

A major rescue operation led by local naturalists was launched to try to save as many chicks as possible. Around 100,000 chicks were thought to have been affected, of which about half certainly died. No less than 27,000 were caught up, their anklets removed, and then released again in a safer area. A sharp tap with a hammer caused the soda to crumble leaving the chick unharmed. In addition, fresh water was pumped into the area to reduce the concentration of soda, and other large creches, totalling some 200,000 chicks, were gently herded away from the most dangerous areas.

This remarkably successful rescue operation is thought to have saved the lives of some 220,000 chicks, probably doubling the number reared at Lake Magadi that year. As this was one of the largest Lesser Flamingo colonies known, it certainly made a very significant difference to the population, particularly as the birds either did not breed or only did so in small numbers for several years thereafter.

Provided the Flamingo chick survives all the hazards and problems of its early life, it then faces a period of years before it is old enough to breed. The only detailed study of Flamingos in the wild which has provided any information on the age at which Flamingos first breed is that in the Camargue. Here young Greater Flamingos have been caught just before fledging for several years and marked with individually numbered plastic rings. These can be read in the field with binoculars or telescope, and so the individual identified in subsequent years.

So far, a very few birds have been proved to at least attempt to breed at four years old, rather more at five years old, and more again at six. However, almost all these birds have been unsuccessful at rearing a chick, and it may be that a Flamingo

Lesser chick with soda 'rings'

has to be seven or eight or even more before it first starts breeding successfully. It should be borne in mind that the Camargue colony is one of the very few where there is regular breeding every year. In other situations, where breeding is erratic and widely spaced, the age of first breeding could be very much more.

CHAPTER 5

Food and Feeding

The unique feeding action of the Flamingo is extremely familiar yet still very strange if one stops and contemplates it. When the head is lowered to the water, it remains in the same position relative to the long neck, as if suspended there upside down, with the crown entering the water first, and the bill pointing backwards. One feels that the bird has only to kick its legs in the air to complete a perfect head-stand. However, having adopted this remarkable stance, the Flamingo has a number of specialised anatomical features to help it to feed in the most efficient manner. But exactly what are the birds feeding on in that muddy water and how, and what differences are there between the various kinds of Flamingo?

Although it is normal to see both Greater and Lesser Flamingos feeding together in the same lakes of Africa, and to find three species, Chilean, Andean, and James', together on South American lakes, they will not be feeding on quite the same foods or taking them in exactly the same way. Certainly there are occasions when two or more different species of birds feed for a while on the same food source, particularly in cases of exceptional abundance, but it is not possible for two species to occupy precisely the same niche all the time; the competition will always drive one of them to extinction or to evolve different habits.

In the case of the Flamingos, there are really quite marked differences between the Greater (and Caribbean) and the Lesser, both in the food that they eat and their method of obtaining it. Similarly, the Chilean differs from the Andean and the James'. The separation of the latter pair is less pronounced, though our knowledge is less, too. The differences are quite fundamental, starting with the structure of the bills themselves. These govern both how the birds take in food, and thus what particular foods they specialise in.

Flamingo bills are of two distinct types, shallow-keeled and deep-keeled. The former kind is found in the larger Flamingos, the Caribbean, Greater, and Chilean, while the three smaller Flamingos, Lesser, Andean, and James', all have deep-keeled bills. The names refer to the shape of the upper mandible. In the shallow-keeled bill, it is as wide as the lower mandible, a flattish oval in cross-section, which when closed does not fully meet the lower mandible – there is a gap along the sides. Inside the mouth there is a considerable space between the jaws, in which lies the long tongue. In the deep-keeled bill, the upper mandible is narrower than the lower one and actually fits between its edges when the bill is closed. Furthermore, the upper mandible is shaped like an equilateral triangle, with the apex of the triangle inside so that it fits snugly into the lower mandible, leaving much less space for the tongue, which occupies a fairly narrow slot.

Both types of bill have considerable areas on the edges and inner surfaces of the mandibles covered in horny thickenings called lamellae. These consist of ridges, often with small teeth, or rows of separated triangular protrusions, which can be raised and lowered at will. Many of the lamellae are in addition fringed with tiny hairs. The shape, numbers, and arrangement of the lamellae vary between the different kinds of Flamingo, and also in different parts of the mouth. It was originally thought that the sole purpose of these lamellae and hairs was to act as a filter, trapping food particles from the mud and water. However, it is now known that while some of them perform this function, others are also acting as excluders, preventing over-sized food particles from even entering the mouth. This latter task is particularly evident in the smaller kinds of Flamingo.

The tongue and the palate are both armed with backward-pointing spines. These help to guide the food towards the throat. The tongue is not moved up and down but rather forward and backward within the groove of the lower mandible, like the piston within a pump. And, like a pump, this produces a sucking action which pulls water into the partly opened bill. As this happens the outer lamellae act as excluders, keeping out objects too large to be treated as food, while the inner lamellae lie flat to allow free passage into the bill of whatever passes the excluders. Then on the return stroke of the tongue, the inner lamellae are raised up, the water is squeezed out past them, and any particles are trapped. If a feeding Flamingo is observed closely, small jets of water can be seen being forced out at the sides of the bill.

The volume of water being sucked in with each pumping action of the tongue has been estimated for the Lesser Flamingo at about 0.5 ml, while slow-motion photography revealed that it was pumping away at about 20 times a second. Much slower rates, of only four or five times every second, have been estimated for the larger Flamingos, though presumably they take in a much greater volume of water each time.

Detailed anatomical studies of the bill structure of the different Flamingos has revealed the sizes of food particles which the lamellae will either exclude or trap. For example, in the Lesser Flamingo, the excluder lamellae have spaces between them measuring about 1.0 x 0.4 millimetres so that anything larger than this will not enter the bill. (A millimetre is approximately four-hundreths of an inch.) The inside lamellae, though, are much closer together and, combined with the fine hairs on them, enclose spaces no more than 0.01 x 0.05 mm. Their principal food therefore must lie between these two sets of measurements. The Caribbean and Greater Flamingos lack excluder lamellae, and only the amount they have their bills open will govern what is taken in, which is usually about 4–6 mm. Inside, the lamellae trap particles down to 0.5 mm. Thus there is remarkably little overlap between the Greater and Lesser Flamingos, so enabling them to feed in the same area, but on different foods.

The differences between the three South American Flamingos have not been studied in the same detail, but it is known that the largest, the Chilean, does indeed take larger food particles than either the Andean or the James'. Indeed, it has much the same sort of mixed diet as the Caribbean and the Greater,

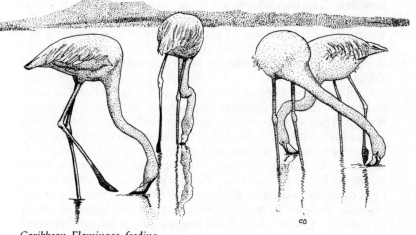

Caribbean Flamingos feeding

having similar filter sizes in its bill. However, the separation between the latter two species is much less, though it does appear as if the James' has finer filters than the Andean, allowing it to take even smaller food particles. Both species feed on diatoms, microscopical plants related to the algae but having a hard cell-wall made of silica. The Andean takes primarily diatoms over 0.8 mm in length, and James' those under 0.6 mm, again demonstrating how the two can co-exist in the same lake.

Just as the gap along the sides of the bill of the Caribbean and Greater Flamingos governs the size of the largest particles which can be taken in, so the smaller Flamingos must not open their bills too wide, otherwise the excluders on the upper and lower mandibles would not meet, thus allowing over-sized objects to enter. It is here that the reason for another conspicuous feature of Flamingo bills becomes apparent. Because of the bend about halfway along the bill, the gap between them stays at a more or less equal width along its entire length when the mandibles are opened. In a straight bill, the gap would widen significantly towards the tip, and so be a much less efficient filtering mechanism. The whole perfectly adapted system of filter-feeding in Flamingos is only matched in the entire vertebrate world by the great whales in the oceans.

Watching the larger and smaller Flamingos feeding reveals further basic differences, which are related to the foods they are eating. The Lesser Flamingo sweeps just the upper surface layers of the water, with only part of its mandibles submerged, to about 3 cm (just over 1 in). Here it finds a blue-green alga called *Spirulina* which is of the right size to be trapped in its lamellae. A further adaptation to its surface-feeding is found in the very bulbous lower mandible. Its interior has a cellular structure, full of airspaces. This effectively acts as a float, so that in choppy water the bill rises and falls with the waves, without the bird having consciously to keep adjusting it to the correct depth.

Caribbean and Greater Flamingos, on the other hand, usually have their heads completely submerged and feed close to the bottom. They sometimes stand in one place paddling with their feet to stir up the mud, but usually walk steadily forwards. They feed on any particles large enough to be trapped in their bills, and these include a wide variety of aquatic invertebrates which might be living in the mud. The brine-shrimp *Artemia* is very important in southern Europe and North Africa, as is the brine-fly *Ephydra* in the Caribbean, while the larvae of many different invertebrates such as chironomids, small molluscs and crustaceans, and some plant seeds, are all eaten.

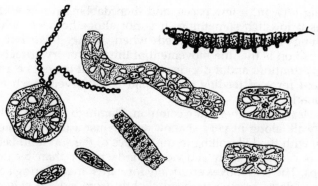

Algae and brine shrimp (not to scale)

It is also possible that these Flamingos may be taking mud from the bottom and filtering this, or even swallowing it wholesale and absorbing nutrition from any bacteria, algae, and organic salts which it may contain. As the head reaches the extreme ends of the swing it is tilted at an angle to the bottom which, as it begins the return swing, would enable it to scoop up the mud.

One feeding method indulged in by the three larger Flamingos is 'treading'. The bird remains more or less in one spot, but turns a circle while at the same time treading vigorously with its feet. Some birds appear to keep their head more or less still and to rotate using it as the central pivot, while others keep their feet treading in the same place while their head describes a circle around them. Either way the effect of stamping with the feet loosens the mud so that the larger objects, such as molluscs and crustaceans, float free and are sucked into the bill.

All the Flamingos will sometimes swim while feeding, when there is too great a depth of water for wading. In addition, they will also upend, though this is much commoner in the larger kinds. They do so in the same way as ducks or swans, though it looks much more ungainly, with their short tail, but rather long legs, sticking up out of the water. In order to maintain this position, the birds usually paddle alternately with their feet, as if trying to swim slowly forwards. This method extends the depth to which they can feed to some 90–100 cm (3 ft), or about 30 cm (1 ft) more than they can reach while wading. It is used by the Caribbean Flamingos in order to feed on the chrysalids of the brine-fly, which live on and under stones and salt encrustations.

Very occasionally, a Flamingo can be seen feeding in shallow water in a manner very similar to that of a Heron, suddenly darting forward a few paces, and then dabbing down with its bill as if to catch something. It is not altogether clear what if anything is actually captured when doing this, but the supposition is that the movement of tiny fish or fry attracts the bird's attention, and it decides to have a go. It cannot be a very efficient form of feeding or it would be observed much more frequently.

The last, and rather more common, Flamingo feeding method is to walk along in very shallow water, just a few centimetres deep, with the bill trailing in the surface of the soft mud below. This is carried out by individual birds rather than by dense groups. The bird moves erratically forwards, meandering across the mudflats, moving its head slightly from side to side as it goes. This method seems to be adopted when the bird is feeding mainly on the mud itself, rather than on solid objects within it. Examination of the mud from an area where this type of feeding had been carried out revealed it contained as much as 20% dry weight of organic matter such as bacteria and blue-green algae.

It is obvious that the presence of enormous numbers, hundreds of thousands or even millions, of Flamingos on one lake must indicate simply phenomenal quantities of food for them. It has been estimated that the daily food requirement of a Lesser Flamingo is about 200 gm (7 oz). This is of fresh algae straight from the water. The standard way of describing food intake is to dry off all the moisture and so obtain the 'dry' weight, which in this case is about 60 gm (2 oz). Half a million Lesser Flamingos, a concentration which has been observed many times, will therefore take approximately 100 tons wet weight (33 tons dry weight) every day.

It is almost impossible to envisage a ton of algae, let alone 100 tons, but it can be seen from these figures that the production of algae in such lakes has to be of stupendous proportions. These microscopic plants have the capacity for extremely rapid reproduction, and can build up to very high densities in the water, to the extent of colouring it green or green-blue. Such concentrations of algae can occur in lakes and reservoirs in Britain, where they are called 'algal blooms'. The combination of a period of hot weather and a high level of nutrients in the water, perhaps washed off adjoining farmland, can stimulate the algae to massive reproduction. In doing so, they may use up such a high proportion of the oxygen in the water that fish and other larger animal life may die. It seems that in the nutrient-rich lakes of the tropics, algal blooms are not only very frequent but may last for many months or even years, to the great benefit of the Flamingos.

Samples of water taken from the surface layers of Lakes Elmenteita and Hannington in East Africa revealed concentrations of algae, after drying thoroughly in an oven, averaging about 3 gm per litre (½ oz per gallon). This means that in order to take in the daily requirement of 60 gm dry weight, each Lesser Flamingo has to filter no less than 20 litres (4.4 gallons) of water. If the concentration of algae in the water falls below 3 gm per litre so the amount of filtering each bird has to do rises, until there comes a point when the bird is having to spend more energy on feeding than it is getting back in the form of food. When this happens the Flamingos will move away, either to another part of the same lake, or to a different lake altogether. It has been suggested that when the algae drop below about 1 gm per litre, they are no longer dense enough for the Lesser Flamingos to feed on successfully.

Somewhat similar calculations have been made for the Caribbean Flamingo in the Netherlands Antilles. Their normal diet is made up of the larvae and chrysalids of the brine-fly. The estimate of daily food intake is put at 270 gm (c.10 oz) dry weight. This is substantially more than a Lesser Flamingo, even allowing for the fact that the latter is only about 60% of the weight of the Caribbean. However, it may also reflect the relative food values of algae and brine-fly larvae and chrysalids.

Brine-fly chrysalids are just a few millimetres long, and have an average weight of about 8 mg. No less than 32,000 of them are needed to make up 270 gm!! The larvae are even smaller, and about 50,000 are equivalent to 270 gm. Because the Caribbean Flamingos feed for only about half of each day, this means that they are having to capture roughly 45 chrysalids or 60 larvae every minute. Assuming, for the sake of simplicity, that only chrysalids are eaten, these figures mean that a flock of 1500 Flamingos, which was the average number present in the study area, would eat 48,000,000 every day, or about one thousand five hundred million per month!

Now, it might be thought that such numbers of brine-flies would be impossible to sustain, that no insect was capable of reproducing sufficiently fast to overcome such heavy predation. But this is to overlook the simple, yet elegant, way in which nature achieves a balance between an animal and its food supply. When a flock of Flamingos arrives at an area of maximum density of brine-fly larvae and chrysalids, they stay in it until they have heavily depleted them, down to about one-third or one-quarter of their original numbers. At this point their feeding becomes relatively inefficient, in a similar manner to the Lesser Flamingos feeding on algae. They therefore leave the area, thus allowing the brine-flies to recover their numbers. And this they can do incredibly quickly. In one area, after the Flamingos had left, chrysalid numbers were at a minimum level, yet within just two weeks numbers were virtually restored to the maximum.

The detailed food requirements of the other kinds of Flamingo have not been worked out as they have for the Lesser and Caribbean, but it is unlikely that they would show any substantial differences. Flamingos are perfectly adapted to feeding on tiny food particles by filtering large quantities of water. They find these in extremely inhospitable places where few other animals or birds can survive. Being highly gregarious birds vast quantities of their chosen food are required, but it is a feature of abnormal or very specialised habitats that the few species that can occur there are able to exist in great abundance simply because there is so little competition. This is as true for the Flamingos as it is for their chosen foods.

One quite unexpected conflict has occurred during the last few years between feeding Flamingos and farmers. In the extensive farmland areas around the marshes and saline lagoons of the Camargue, there has been a considerable increase recently in the amount of land devoted to growing rice. The shallowly-flooded fields were gradually discovered by the Flamingos, and when they were seen feeding in them it was a reasonable assumption that they were taking invertebrates from the water and muddy soil. However, the farmers began to accuse them of taking the newly-sown rice grains, and even though this seemed to be highly unlikely, more seriously accused them of damaging the young sprouting rice plants by trampling them underfoot. The examination of a few stomachs of birds found dead under wires confirmed that the bulk of the food was indeed invertebrates, and while there was some rice present this could well have been taken by accident, during the normal sifting process.

Some of the local farmers attempted to obtain permission to shoot the Flamingos as a means of preventing damage to their crops. Local biologists studying the species resisted this move and instead first persuaded the French Government to fund the systematic scaring of the birds and then themselves put a great deal of effort into keeping the birds away from the fields. Much of the feeding was taking place at night, so flares, flashing lights, and carbide bangers were brought in and a concerted programme of scaring was mounted at the critical period of a few weeks from sowing. This proved to be very successful and within a couple of years the farmers had taken on the job themselves, and pressure to shoot the birds virtually disappeared.

Not all conflicts between birds and agriculture end so amicably, but this can be regarded as a classic case of good cooperation bringing about satisfactory results for all parties. It must be hoped that this remains a unique instance of this highly specialised bird adapting itself to such an artificial feeding environment where it can, even unwittingly, cause damage to man's crops.

CHAPTER 6

Flamingos and Man

As we saw in the first chapter, Man has exploited Flamingos for thousands of years, just as he has exploited almost all other kinds of wildlife. Any highly gregarious and colonially nesting bird is likely to be regarded as a source of meat and eggs by local people. This type of exploitation has undoubtedly been carried on since Man evolved as a hunter/gatherer. He became just another predator on the Flamingos, which relied for the same defence against him as they did against four-legged predators, namely the harsh and remote terrain in which they live.

Down to very recent times, certainly in the last thirty years, local villagers in both Spain and France have gathered eggs from Greater Flamingo colonies. They no doubt regarded this as a perfectly legitimate practice, just as their ancestors had done before them, taking advantage of the bonus supply of food in those relatively infrequent years when these fickle breeders chose to nest in their area. A number of recent breeding attempts in Tunisia have also been subject to egg-collecting, while as one moves to more remote areas, with greater numbers of people close to the subsistence level, so the taking of eggs, young, and also adult Flamingos, becomes more commonplace. Some of the South American breeding colonies are robbed on a regular basis and certainly have been for centuries.

Slaughtering large numbers of adults, then extracting their tongues in order to serve them as a delicacy at banquets is, perhaps, something too typically Roman to worry about a recurrence. Yet, mass killing of Flamingos for food has occurred in a number of parts of the world down to quite recent times. In parts of the Caribbean, moulting birds and their young would be driven into nets by local villagers using dogs. And this was certainly still happening only 30 years ago.

However, it is one thing to take eggs, young, or adults for food, if you are living at or near subsistence level, and quite another to hunt them for sport. There are a number of published accounts of 'sportsmen' shooting Flamingos, 'bringing down

Andean Flamingos and chicks

seven birds with a single shot', with Flamingos driven over the guns like Pheasants. Wealthy sportsmen from Britain, France, and Italy, visiting some of the more remote areas around the Mediterranean, would enlist the help of locals to provide sport shooting of whatever wildlife was present. And if there was insufficient enjoyment in the hunting of a particular species, then at least some trophies had been obtained to take back home.

Man has also caused the deaths of many Flamingos for another, not wholly justifiable reason, namely the keeping of Flamingos in captivity purely as a public spectacle. Only very recently has such a purpose been gradually abandoned, though as yet only in a proportion of zoos, in favour of a policy of trying to establish captive breeding colonies. The ultimate aim is to be able to produce enough young to satisfy the needs of zoos and bird gardens, so that no more Flamingos need be taken from the wild. There is still a long way to go before it is completely successful, but at least it is being tried.

It is likely that Flamingos have been kept in captivity for many centuries. Indeed, the Romans are known to have kept them, and it is possible that the Ancient Egyptians did too, much earlier. When the keeping and exhibiting of strange animals and birds in cages became popular in Europe, in the eighteenth century, Flamingos were certainly included in some of the menageries. They easily fulfilled the necessary criteria of being weird and wonderful to look at, yet with little or nothing known about them in the wild. Their occurrence in southern Europe probably meant that they were fairly easy to obtain.

There followed two centuries of Flamingos being kept in captivity, with no better purpose than as exhibits for public entertainment. The idea that a primary purpose of zoos should be to breed different animals and birds in captivity, as a contribution towards their conservation, is a very recent one. The first ever breeding of Flamingos in captivity was in 1937, when a single Caribbean Flamingo egg was hatched at the Hialeah racetrack, Florida. The chick did not survive very long, and it was five years before there was better success. It was not until 1957 that a second kind of Flamingo was successfully bred in captivity, when a Chilean Flamingo hatched at Philadelphia Zoo. The same zoo also hatched the first Greater Flamingo, in 1961, while the first Andean Flamingo to breed was at the Wildfowl Trust, Slimbridge, in 1969. The Lesser Flamingo has yet to breed successfully, though eggs have been laid at a few zoos in recent years, including at Slimbridge, where the James' Flamingo laid for the first time in 1985, though none of the three eggs was fertile.

There are a number of problems associated with breeding Flamingos in captivity, some of which have recently been at least partially solved. The first requirement is that the birds must be in excellent condition, with their plumage as well coloured as possible. For years, before the relationship between diet and the colouring of the feathers was properly understood, newly-captured Flamingos had faded quite quickly and then remained nearly white. Without the necessary pigment in their food, there was no possibility for them to regain more than a shadow of their true red and pink plumage. Even now, when the proper food additives are readily available, one often sees extremely pale and washed-out Flamingos in bird gardens and zoos, whose owners have either failed to understand about the correct diet or do not care anyway.

It is also obviously very important that there are enough birds. This is not as silly as it sounds. Flamingos are very gregarious birds and always breed in colonies. We saw in an earlier chapter that some of their mass displays are almost certainly involved in stimulating large numbers of birds to breed simultaneously. It is equally likely that unless there are sufficient number of birds taking part in the displays that they will not have the desired effect. Generally speaking, the zoos with the largest flocks of Flamingos have the most successful breeding record.

There are one or two instances of nesting by Caribbean Flamingos when there were less than 10 birds present, but normally at least 15–20 birds seem to be needed and preferably more. The exception provided by the Caribbean Flamingo is quite interesting because this is the one kind of Flamingo that, at least on the Galapagos, does nest in tiny colonies, often of under 10 pairs.

Zoos and bird gardens have adopted a number of different methods of enlarging their Flamingos flocks. Firstly, and most obviously, they have obtained more birds from the wild. This aspect will be discussed further below. Secondly, it is now becoming more usual for zoos to loan or exchange some of their stock. Thus, instead of there being several zoos each with a handful of one of the rarer Flamingos, such as Andean or James', and no possibility of getting them to breed, there could be one or two with a reasonably large flock which would have a considerable potential for breeding. And once regular breeding has been achieved, then the progeny can be used to restock the remaining zoos.

The third method open to zoos to increase their Flamingo flocks is to put all their Flamingos, regardless of species, together in one pen. This can have the desired effect of stimulating breeding, but it also can have one highly undesirable side-effect, namely the production of hybrid young. This has happened a number of times, most often involving Caribbean and Greater, or Caribbean and Chilean, but there has been at least one Caribbean x Andean hybrid produced, too. This makes a nonsense of any captive breeding programme, as the hybrids are usually relatively infertile, and anyway can add nothing to future stocks.

Much thought and effort has been put into ensuring that the right conditions are provided for the birds to breed. This is perhaps not as critical as was once thought, when elaborate measures were taken to ensure that mud of exactly the right consistency was available in the nesting enclosure. There are several regularly breeding groups of captive Flamingos which ignore the nice, wet and muddy areas of their pens, and instead make their nests on areas of grass or bare earth. This is, after all, how some of them breed in the wild.

Most Flamingo enclosures contain rather more land than water, though there is enormous variation, and they also vary very greatly in size, so this is probably not too critical. What does seem important is that the birds are able to retreat some distance from the public if they wish to. It is certainly a fact that nearly all the nesting sites in zoo enclosures are rather further

away from the public than areas where the birds may feed or stand around.

Many zoos provide artificial nest mounds, made with mud or even concrete, in an attempt to stimulate the birds to build their own. This is of doubtful value, though it may have helped some colonies to make a start. Once successful breeding has taken place, the birds will nearly always nest in the same spot in subsequent years, even if the old nests have been completely removed.

Although the South American Flamingos regularly encounter freezing temperatures and even ice-covered water at times, none of the six kinds are really hardy, and all the zoos and bird gardens in temperate regions provide their Flamingos with heated quarters for the winter. One problem here is that if the ground inside the winter house is not to get indescribably muddy, then it has to be concreted over, and standing on such a surface for weeks on end can produce abrasions and cuts on the birds' feet, which in turn may become infected. Covering the concrete with tough polythene seems to provide a satisfactory solution.

Even when all the conditions are apparently ideal, the Flamingos may still not settle down and breed. One other problem for which there has only very recently been a solution has been knowing the sex of the birds in the flock. Males are larger than females on the whole, but there is quite an overlap, particularly among the smaller kinds. Some zoos have suspected that a failure by their Flamingos to breed has been because of an imbalance of the sexes. As one cannot sex Flamingos cloacally, as one can ducks or geese, this was almost insoluble. Now, however, a trained vet can insert a tiny optical fibre probe into the body cavity, through a tiny slit made in the wall of the abdomen. It is then possible to see whether the bird possesses ovaries or testes.

When the flock of about 60 Lesser Flamingos at the Wildfowl Trust at Slimbridge was sexed using the optical probe, it was found that there were twice as many males as females. Twenty of each were therefore selected to form the main flock, while the 20 surplus males were put in a different enclosure. It was at least possible that the excess of males had led to rather more harassment of the females than would be normal, perhaps putting them off attempting to breed. Only time will tell whether this theory is right. Lesser Flamingos have still to breed successfully in captivity, though eggs have been laid at Slimbridge, as at one or two other zoos.

Mention was made above of how zoos might enlarge their flocks of Flamingos by obtaining more from the wild. This practice is now no longer quite so easy as it once was, thanks to the welcome restrictions on trade in wild animals and birds that are now coming into force. It is a fact, though, that many tens of thousands of Flamingos have been captured and transported to zoos and bird gardens all over the world, and another fact that many more will have died during capture or, more probably, during what can often be a very long journey, in both distance and time, between where they were caught and their final destination.

There are rather few statistics available but a survey in the early 1970s revealed that there were over 2500 Flamingos in a sample of 35 zoos which had successfully bred at least one kind. While they might reasonably be thought to have larger flocks of Flamingos than other zoos, they represent only a small fraction of the estimated 1200 zoos in the world, not to mention the countless small bird gardens and private bird collections. At least half of the official zoos have Flamingos on show, so the overall numbers in captivity must be very large indeed.

The number of Flamingos ever reared in captivity is between

1000 and 1500, so it is obvious that these can go only a little way towards providing the numbers needed for all the different zoos. One has to bear in mind that several hundred birds will die each year and most zoos will want to replace losses in order to retain Flamingos in their collections, and unless they are very successful at breeding, these replacements will have to come from the wild.

Accurate figures on the numbers of Flamingos being taken from the wild are very hard to come by. However, the United States Government has published figures for the numbers of birds and mammals imported into that country in the five-year period 1968–1972. During this time a total of no less than 2551 Flamingos were brought in. It is not possible to get a complete breakdown of the different kinds of Flamingo involved, as some of the names, taken from the import licences, are not sufficiently detailed. In 1970, for example, 40 birds just described as 'Flamingos' were imported from Argentina. It is fairly certain that these were Chilean, but just possible that they were Andean instead, or even a mixture. However, allowing for such inadequacies, it appears that in those five years, 1378 Caribbean, 1081 Chilean, 38 James', 34 Greater, and 20 Lesser Flamingos were imported into the United States. At that same time, just ten zoos in the United States had successfully bred Flamingos.

A similar picture, though on a slightly smaller scale, would no doubt emerge for Britain and Europe if the figures were available. Certainly, several hundreds have come into Britain in some years, with a larger preponderance of Greaters and Lessers, as these are geographically nearer and so rather more available. When the Wildfowl Trust first started receiving wild-caught Flamingos in the early 1960s, mortality within a few days or weeks of arrival was particularly high, caused no doubt by the stress of the journey. Transporting these birds is quite difficult, with no general agreement as to the best way, whether confined by some kind of restrictive jacket, or allowed to stand in a sufficiently large, but well-padded crate.

The capture of Flamingos from the wild still goes on, but gradually more and more countries are curtailing the activities of the people trading in live birds, whether by banning it altogether, or by at least insisting on the highest possible standards of handling throughout the operation. The long-term aim of all zoos must be to breed all their desirable animals and birds so successfully that numbers in captivity become self-maintaining, removing for ever the need to take more from the wild.

This laudable position has been reached at least locally with the Chilean Flamingo. The Wildfowl Trust has been able to provide sizeable flocks for two of its other centres produced entirely by the breeding colony at Slimbridge. The Greater Flamingo and Caribbean Flamingos, too, breed quite regularly in captivity and will soon reach the point when there will be surplus young that can be used to replenish or found other flocks. For the other three kinds, though, there still seems a long way to go, yet, unhappily, two of these, the Andean and the James', are also the rarest kinds in the world, and so just the ones not to go on catching in the wild.

In the last few decades, Flamingos have been given legal protection in many countries where they occur. This caused little hardship to people in Spain and France who were involved to collecting eggs; they have a sufficiently high standard of living to be able to do without this particular source of food. In many other countries, however, this may not be true and it becomes difficult to justify a ban on such traditional harvesting, which has probably had little or no effect on Flamingo numbers despite being carried on for hundreds of years.

If it was just a question of enabling indigenous peoples, such as the Indians of the High Andes, to continue their age-old way of life, then there need be no real problem. When it does become harder to countenance, though, is if instead of collecting eggs for their own consumption these traditional gatherers take them for selling to the people in neighbouring towns and cities. The need for protein in urban slums can be as great if not greater than in the rural areas, but such trading with Flamingo eggs has moved the whole process away from taking an apparently sustainable harvest for strictly local use, to a situation where there is a tangible reward for gathering as many eggs as possible. While a Flamingo colony might well be able to withstand the original level of egg loss, even slightly increasing the number removed could easily spell disaster within a very few years.

In an ideal world, it would be possible to permit continued taking of eggs by local peoples, up to a level that regular monitoring showed the colony or population could sustain. Alas, as must be clear by now, our knowledge of even the approximate numbers of Flamingos in several parts of the world is very sketchy, let alone rising to such detailed information as the annual productivity needed to maintain overall populations, and hence the number of eggs that could safely be taken without harmful effect.

Merely pronouncing that Flamingos are protected in a particular country or region is hardly enough, of course. It is also necessary to inform and educate the population of this fact, and to enforce the law. It seems unlikely that much progress can be made in this direction in several countries where Flamingos occur; there are other more urgent priorities for the Governments concerned. Lacking adequate knowledge, it is also very hard for national or international conservation bodies to give the proper advice. Just telling a Government that the Flamingos in their country should be protected because they may be in danger of being over-exploited is hardly enough. It is up to the same conservationists to fund the obtaining of sufficient knowledge on which to base good advice. And this should not only be into the biology of Flamingos, but equally into the needs of the local people.

To conclude this chapter on the relationships between Flamingos and Man on a more cheerful note, there have been a number of examples of active conservation and management of Flamingo haunts which have undoubtedly contributed enormously to their well-being, if not actual survival. Two of these stand out: firstly, the creation of a sanctuary breeding area for Caribbean Flamingos on Bonaire in the Netherlands Antilles, when it looked as though the conversion of the large natural saline lagoon where they bred into a salt works would complete destroy all the natural habitat; and secondly, the successful construction of an artificial nesting island in the Camargue after the original island had become almost completely eroded away, coupled with a number of other important conservation measures.

'The Flamingos on Bonaire' is the title of a scientific report written by the Dutch ornithologist Jan Rooth in 1965. He studied the Caribbean Flamingos breeding on Bonaire in great detail, discovering much that was new about their habitat, diet, and breeding biology. At that time, the breeding site was in a 500 hectare (1200 acre) natural saline lagoon. The birds were subject to some interference from local people, formerly through egg-collecting and the hunting of both young and old birds, as well as, more recently, disturbance caused by low-flying aircraft.

It is an unfortunate habit, which has been noted in several different areas where Flamingos occur, that pilots of light aircraft, perhaps urged on by their passengers, seem possessed of an irresistible urge to fly low over the masses of birds and so flush them into the air. In one or two areas this has become almost a sport, and is deliberately indulged in for the benefit of camera-happy tourists. It is, of course, potentially disastrous to the Flamingos, especially if they are on eggs at the time.

The situation on Bonaire, though, was reasonably good. Flamingos were known to have bred there since 1681, and the

degree of protection that had been afforded the birds since the 1940s had allowed 2000-3000 pairs to breed successfully in most years. The food supply in the salt-lake, mainly brine-fly chrysalids, was at times inadequate for all the breeding birds which were present, forcing them either to filter organic material out of the mud, as described in Chapter 5, or to make a feeding flight to the coast of Venezuela, a round trip of 280 km (155 miles). Nevertheless, this seemed not to affect adversely the rearing of the young.

Then in the mid-1960s, it was proposed to build a saltworks in the lagoon, also taking in a large area of adjoining low-lying ground. Because the proposal involved maintaining higher water-levels the main breeding site was going to disappear. Fortunately it proved possible for an agreement to be reached between the conservationists concerned about this, the only regular breeding site in the whole of the southern Caribbean, and the company wanting to extract salt. A 55 hectare (130 acre) sanctuary was set aside in the midst of the much larger area, over 2000 ha (4800 acres) of evaporation pools. Although very small, it represented a compromise between the absolute minimum requirement biologically and the maximum that the company felt economically able to bear.

The sanctuary was created by building a dyke all round it, as low and rounded as possible so that the Flamingos would be able to walk to and from the adjoining condensation lagoons. In addition two pumps were installed so that the water level within the sanctuary could be controlled. This was considered vital, as with all the levels raised in the surrounding lagoons, the sanctuary would be very liable to flood after heavy rains. At the same time it was important not to let the sanctuary dry out and so cause the mud to harden and become unsuitable for nest building.

The Flamingos found the sanctuary very soon after it was completed, and were actually nesting inside it within a few months. And they have continued to do so ever since. There have been some problems, mainly with the food supply. The construction of the saltworks has increased the salinity in the lagoons, and while it was originally thought that this would benefit the Flamingos by increasing the habitat suitable for the brine-fly, an unforeseen development has been the settling out of gypsum and other carbonates on to the bottom of the lagoons, producing a crust. This covers the former soft mud and so is unsuitable either for brine-flies or feeding Flamingos. The latter now fly even more regularly than before to Venezuela.

There are several species of small snail now flourishing in some of the salt lagoons and the Flamingos have been feeding on them to some extent, but sudden changes in salinity which occur from time to time seem to cause massive fluctuations in snail numbers, so that it is not a reliable food supply.

The Bonaire sanctuary is an obvious success story. Firstly, it proved possible for conservationists and a strictly commercial interest to come to a mutually agreed solution. Secondly, that solution has been proved to work. The construction of the lagoons and the sanctuary caused minimal interruption to the regular pattern of Flamingo breeding, and while there have been some changes in the food supply, the birds have managed to find alternatives when needed. There is still probably some improvement required in the protection afforded to the whole lagoon complex, particularly to reduce all forms of disturbance, but that apart the future of the Caribbean Flamingos on Bonaire seems assured.

This is also true of the Greater Flamingos in the Camargue. Here there is also a long tradition of breeding, though as explained in Chapter 2 it was often intermittent with long periods of little or no success, or of no attempts at all. A large part of the Rhone Delta has long been a saltworks, with many condensation lagoons providing the high salinity needed to produce sufficient food for the Flamingos. The birds have never had a specific sanctuary area set aside for them, but their requirement for an island to nest on restricted their choice of lagoon to a very few.

The island which they used during the 1950s and early 1960s

gradually eroded away. The very act of nest construction lowers the level of the island, and makes both flooding and further erosion from wave action all the greater. So the Flamingos are actually responsible for the destruction of their own vital habitat. In more natural conditions, the water level would be much lower for most of the year than it is allowed to be in the lagoons, and wave action in particular would be much less damaging. In these artificial circumstances, however, the life of the island is severely curtailed.

The 1962 and 1963 breeding seasons were almost complete failures, with very high egg losses and mortality of chicks. There followed five years, 1964 to 1968, with no breeding attempted. The island at the original site had eroded very badly and it seemed that the Flamingos had decided that it was no longer suitable. However, they were apparently also extremely reluctant to try out a new site. It was not until 1969 that they adopted an island in the Fangassier Lagoon, but when they did so it was one of their best years ever, with over 7000 pairs rearing 6000 young.

However, good though the new island was, it could not hold all the 7000 pairs, but only some 4900. The remainder nested on a much smaller, and lower, island in the same lagoon, where the nests were very vulnerable to flooding and wave action, or at the foot of the encircling dyke, open to disturbance and predation. It was therefore decided, by the local biologists and conservationists, to improve the conditions for the Flamingos by increasing the area of safe nesting island available to them.

The existing main island was left alone, partly to avoid any disturbance to what had been a highly successful breeding site, and partly because it was surrounded by extremely soft mud. However, adjoining the smaller island the mud was firmer and it was possible to drain the lagoon and then bring in a bulldozer. This scraped up mud into an island of approximately 6200 square metres (7200 square yards), projecting about 40 cm (16 in) above the normal summer water level. The banks were carefully graded, so that the Flamingos could walk up and down them easily.

It was rather frustrating after all the hard work that had gone into the new island when the Flamingos completely ignored it for the next four years. They continued to breed each year, twice on the main island, and twice elsewhere when extra high water levels prevented them using it. The overspill was scattered in other areas. Then in 1973, recalling the regular practice in zoos, some 300 artificial nests were made on the specially constructed island using up-turned buckets of mud, and a further 200 genuine nests were moved from their situation at the foot of the dyke.

The effect of this action was dramatic. In 1974, the main colony was on the usual island, but the overspill all nested on and among the artificial nests on the new island. The following year, after some more artificial nests had been put out, the number of nests on the new island rose to 2900. By 1976, when the original island had become so badly eroded that there was only room for about half the 1969 total of nests, the main colony had shifted to the new island, where it has remained ever since. About 10,500 nests were occupied on the island in 1982, easily the largest single colony recorded in the Camargue. Because the island is fairly close to a corner of the lagoon, it receives quite a lot of shelter from the surrounding dykes, so that erosion from wave action has been much slower than on the other islands that have been used for nesting.

The Camargue Flamingos have received other beneficial attentions. The colony is wardened throughout the breeding season, to prevent accidental or deliberate disturbance, whether by over-keen birdwatchers and photographers, or uninformed tourists. In addition, the population of Herring Gulls in the area has been reduced, to cut down on their predation of eggs and young. Agreements have also been reached with the relevant authorities to ban over-flying aircraft, especially during the breeding season. The unbroken run of successful breeding attempts since 1969 speaks for itself as a measure of the equal success of this conservation effort.

Flamingos will always hold a great appeal, whether for the committed conservationist, or just the ordinary visitor to a zoo. They are naturally great survivors, able to live in conditions so harsh that few other animals can share them. This has ensured their continued existence down to the present day, and gives

some hope for the future. Man has destroyed so much natural habitat in the world, and continues to do so at an increasing rate. However, the vast salt-lakes and saline mud-flats of the tropics must be safer than most from this kind of exploitation, while as we have seen, it is possible to carry out at least some developments of them without completely ruining them for the Flamingos.

The greatest threats to Flamingos are probably those associated with increasing human populations requiring any available source of protein, and this kind of pressure is among the hardest to resist. However, while it may not be too far into the future when we have all six kinds of Flamingos producing self-sustaining flocks in captivity, and while this gives the largest number of everyday people the chance to see these marvellous birds, there is no doubt that we have a very strong responsibility to ensure that the spectacle of Flamingos in their tens and hundreds of thousands, the pink foam along a lake shore, must always be there for those fortunate enough to be able to see it.

Further Reading

It is a sad fact that all the books so far written on Flamingos are out of print. This includes both the serious scientific works, and the more popular accounts of the pioneer discoverers of Flamingo habits and biology. However, as they all turn up on the second-hand market from time to time, they are listed here for those who, perhaps stimulated by this book, wish to take their interest in Flamingos a little further.

Etienne Gallet, *The Flamingos of the Camargue* (Blackwell, Oxford, 1950)
This is a poetic account of one man's passion for the Greater Flamingos in the south of France. There are many nuggets of information but they are scattered through much descriptive and occasionally anthropomorphic writing. There are several exceptionally fine black and white photographs.

G.K. Yeates, *Flamingo City* (Country Life, 1950)
George Yeates visited the Camargue in 1947 and 1948 to photograph the birds there, and made particular efforts to find a breeding colony of Flamingos, helped by Etienne Gallet. Two chapters, and many photographs, are devoted to the Flamingos, and there is also a long and detailed appendix reviewing the then state of knowledge of Flamingos throughout the world.

Robert Allen, *The Flamingos: their life history and survival* (the National Audubon Society, New York, 1956)
This is a very detailed and readable account, principally of the Caribbean Flamingo, but with many fascinating details of the past history of all six kinds. More recent studies have made some of the results and conclusions out of date, but there is still much of interest here, perhaps particularly on the historical side.

Leslie Brown, *The Mystery of the Flamingos* (Country Life, 1959)

This is Leslie Brown's description of his six-year search for the breeding grounds of the Lesser Flamingo, of his discoveries, his many frustrations, and how he nearly lost his life in the process. It is profusely illustrated with black and white photographs.

Janet Kear and Nicole Duplaix-Hall (eds.), *Flamingos* (T. & A.D. Poyser, 1975)
The proceedings of the symposium held at Slimbridge in 1973. It contains papers on numbers, distribution, and conservation across the world, on many aspects of catching and keeping Flamingos in captivity, on behaviour, and on the mechanisms by which Flamingos obtain pigment from their food and deposit it in their feathers. There are appendices of weights and measurements, and numerous colour and black and white photographs.

In addition to the above books, there are many published papers in major ornithological and wildlife journals, including *Ibis*, *Journal of the Bombay Natural History Society*, *Journal of East African Wildlife Society*, and *Ostrich*. There is a bibliography of several hundred titles in Robert Allen's book, and one of over 300, mainly post-war, in 'Flamingos'. The Flamingo Working Group of I.C.B.P.–I.W.R.B. produces an occasional Newsletter, which lists recent literature. The Old World Co-ordinator of the Group is Dr Alan Johnson at the Tour du Valat, Arles, France.

Index